LUKEWARMING

The New
Climate Science
That Changes
Everything

LUKEWARMING

Patrick J. Michaels
AND
Paul C. Knappenberger

CATO
INSTITUTE
WASHINGTON, D.C.

eBook ISBN: 978-1-939709-95-0
Print ISBN: 978-1-939709-96-7

Library of Congress Cataloging-in-Publication Data available.

Cover design: John Meyers.
Printed in the United States of America.

Cato Institute
1000 Massachusetts Avenue, N.W.
Washington, D.C. 20001
www.cato.org

Contents

Acknowledgments

Many people have helped with this book. They include Cato Institute vice president John Samples who suggested it be written after Matt Ridley published "My Life as a Lukewarmer" in the *Times* (London) on January 19, 2015. Ridley accurately portrays the difficulty of being a moderate in a climate of extremes. John, who is the best professional adviser I've ever had, suggested I write about the science supporting the middle-of-the-road perspective concerning climate change. I believe the evidence is strong—and growing stronger—that the denouement of the climate issue will be lukewarm not only in terms of policy, but also in temperature.

Global warming gets persistently distorted (as do a number of other scientific fields) by an incentive structure that awards money and advancement for loudly proclaimed science and flashy results. Such science largely is funded by a government that expects something in return. Scientists "get" that message without being told: provide support for our policies and your issue will continue to be opulently funded; you will receive tenure and never again fly in coach. The horrifically bad U.S. National Climate Assessments of climate change are Exhibits One, Two, and Three in all of this, as is detailed in this book.

Researchers now are showing that these problems aren't limited to climate science. The philosophical foundation for this book stands on the work of Stanford University's Daniele Fanelli and John Ioannidis and the University of Virginia's Brian Nosek, who are documenting the decrepitation of society's canon of knowledge. Terence Kealey—a great friend, true gentleman, and scholar—also encouraged me to look at this large and disturbing picture.

Ed Crane, Cato Institute's former CEO, has been my best supporter and fostered Cato Institute's new Center for the Study of Science. It may seem odd, but many in the libertarian world naively believe that science is where truth dwells, and Crane, in his inimitable fashion, ended the debate as to whether Cato Institute should study this.

John Allison, Ed's successor, made sure the vulnerable Center for the Study of Science lived well and prospered as it became more established during Cato Institute's leadership transition. John and Ed are polar opposites in management style, but both have been wonderfully supportive, often in the face of considerable opposition.

Thanks also to Princeton University physics professor Will Happer, another true gentleman in a world of scientific brutes, for providing backup power when my science would inexplicably flame out. The original version of this manuscript contained a mistake on radiative transfer and he caught it. Happer is a physics scholar in the best tradition of his university, an institution that seems to have lost its way in so many other fields. Where are more Happers when we need them so much? Thanks as well to Judith Curry, professor of earth and atmospheric science at the Georgia Institute of Technology, for a critical read and very helpful suggestions as the manuscript was struggling through puberty.

David Wojick, with his doctorate in history and the philosophy of science, once labored in the belly of the beast at the U.S. Department of Energy. He has provided valuable insights (and text!) about the way governments and environmental scientists interact. At a more basic level, Khristine Brookes and Joe Verruni at Cato Institute provide invaluable philosophical advice on how to really communicate. I am also indebted to my coauthor Paul C. (Chip) Knappenberger, who understands the technicalities of climate science better than anyone I know. The world of climate science knows he is among the best—ever.

Then there's Rachel. I always think my first drafts are great. She disagrees and makes them much better. Prior to the showing of institutional support for the new science center, she strongly encouraged me to broaden my study of science horrors beyond the climate change issue. She thought it a good idea that I seek out scholars who could help me do so.

Now I hate this phrase, but I'm going to "circle back" to Ridley. Besides being the inspiration for this book, he has played a much larger role in my life than he may know, for better or worse.

Back when I could still terrorize rightfielders in amateur softball, Rachel was playing on Cato's co-rec team and lost a front tooth to a hot grounder. She thought the guy ministering to her was kinda cute. In graduate school at the University of Glasgow, she'd been introduced to—and was quite taken with—Ridley's *Origins of Virtue*. I asked her if she'd like to meet him, thereby earning myself some cred. When this revised edition is published, Rachel and I will have been married in Scotland.

Pat Michaels
Marshall, Virginia

Introduction

> If present trends continue, the world will be . . . eleven
> degrees colder by the year 2000. This is about twice what it
> would take to put us in an ice age.
>
> —Kenneth E. F. Watt*

Our national political discourse is about as polarized as it has
been since the Civil War and it is affecting all sorts of issues—foreign policy, group rights, and health care, to name a few. Likewise
for global warming, the media sorts people into "alarmist" or "denier" camps—words needing little further explication.[1] But there's
a third group not as visible, not as extreme, and yet possessed with
substantial explanatory power of which the public is, at best, only
vaguely aware. These are the "lukewarmers." That's us.

The lukewarm synthesis of global warming is simple. Increasing
concentrations of carbon dioxide and other greenhouse gases exert
a mild warming pressure on the lower atmosphere. This has been
known for 150 years. But lukewarmers have been aware for some
time that something isn't right with the climate projections made by
general circulation climate models. Nearly 30 years ago, it became
obvious that the models were predicting far too much warming in
response to carbon dioxide changes. Lukewarmers believe the evidence of some human-caused climate change is compelling, but it is
hardly the alarming amount predicted by the models.

Lukewarmers tend to be science watchers who have an inherent
interest in the processes of the profession. We are concerned about
the unquestioning attitude of the many climate modelers who have
testified to the U.S. Congress about their forecasts. Given the general
knowledge that the models have been too hot, the modelers have

---

* Kenneth E. F. Watt is an author and professor emeritus of evolution and ecology
at the University of California–Davis. This quotation comes from his address during
the first Earth Day celebration in 1970.

[1] Make no mistake, "denier" is a very loaded word, and when it is invoked, many
writers frequently place "holocaust" somewhere nearby.

supplied some other factor that cools them down. Most lukewarmers thought the application of such a competing emission—sulfate aerosol—was an obvious Band-Aid because it allowed modelers to simulate the past as perfectly as they wanted. The possible range of sulfate cooling effects is so large that any value that fits the past could (and would) be selected. Historians of science have extensively documented how difficult it is for scientists to abandon their paradigms (in this case, the notion of a disastrous warming). Sulfate aerosol has allowed climate modelers to hold onto their paradigm far longer than is warranted.

Newer, more robust estimates of the sulfate cooling effect are disclosing what the lukewarmers long suspected—namely, that the sulfates are more of a cheap fix than an explanatory reality. The truth is that the various families of climate models are just too darned hot or, to put it in the jargon of the day, their sensitivity to carbon dioxide is too high.

So it follows that climate policies based on those models similarly are too "hot." Moreover, the human nature of the modeling community impedes the utterance of life's three most important words: we were wrong. Consequently, those who study the effects of climate change continue to produce a florid literature of alarming climate change impacts. When summarized in various government compendia—perhaps for use by a regulatory agency like the U.S. Environmental Protection Agency—the picture therefore always is alarming and is likely to be wrong. Lukewarmers are aware of this problem and tend to be skeptical of the "impacts" literature. This book provides myriad examples of the misuse of the hot models and the tremendous incentives that exist for their continued misuse.

World governments gathered in Paris in December 2015 and finally—after six years of failure—produced a new international agreement on global warming. President Obama was instrumental in this process as a true believer in the alarmist view of global warming and views his role in advancing the climate agenda as a key element of his legacy. Obama's science adviser is John Holdren, a longtime environmental doomsayer who has subscribed to and touted every failed environmental apocalypse. The President isn't a scientist and lacks a scientific bent, so he depends on Holdren, despite his track record.

This book, *Lukewarming*, begins with the basic evidence for lukewarming and the historical development of the lukewarm synthesis. We then segue to the meeting in Paris and what happened there.

Georgia Institute of Technology's Judith Curry, building upon the work of Harvard's Cass Sunstein, provides us with a model that explains the phenomenal and systematic distortion accompanying the issue of global warming. Curry and Sunstein write of an "availability cascade," an echo chamber in which issues transmogrify from obscurity into grand narratives. Once an availability cascade is established, a host of horrors follow. Only in such a world could people seriously blame the ghoulish beheadings and serial massacres by ISIS on—of all things—global warming. We have models, compendia, and an availability cascade—so we must be right. We detail a number of issues descending from this particular availability cascade.[2]

We show how the incentive structure in modern science was established soon after World War II and led to the federal takeover of much of science (and all of climate science) and how that can create a systematic distortion in the direction of alarmism. We go into considerable detail concerning the resulting summary documents that serve as the basis for alarmist policies, concentrating on the three National Assessments of global warming impacts on the United States.[3]

Even in a culture of alarmism, science still is sufficiently individualistic. Some researchers, often not beholden to a federal master, have hacked away at the overly hot models. We detail that

---

[2] Arguments are based upon a paper further analyzed in Chapter 8: Colin P. Kelley et al., "Climate Change in the Fertile Crescent and Implications of the Recent Syrian Drought," *Proceedings of the National Academy of Sciences* 112 (2015): 3241–46.

[3] An important note on terminology: The three U.S. National Climate Assessments referenced in this book are produced by the same federal conglomerate of agencies that disburses climate research funding. The name of this entity changes every few years for reasons no one understands. For convenience and to minimize reader confusion, we tend to use only one name for that entity—U.S. Global Change Research Program (USGCRP). No matter the name, the same people and their successors largely are responsible for preparing the assessments. In our view, the assessments can be considered compendia showcasing everything that is wrong with the way politically larded science is funded and practiced.

progression and note how little it has influenced the policy process. Availability cascades are hard to break.

Borrowing a phrase from science writer Matt Ridley, we segue to the "rational optimism" of lukewarmers. Despite the continued cadence of alarm and the endless parade of environmental alarmists, increasing carbon dioxide is creating a greener planet and more food and is taking plants back to their genetic roots—a world of higher carbon dioxide concentration that allows them to flourish under increasingly high temperature. It's logical that a slightly warmer world with an increased atmospheric concentration of carbon dioxide will be a richer one.

But the drumbeat continues. Near the end of the book, we put down most of the "weather is getting worse" myths—and myths they are. We pay special attention to the one true nightmare with regard to global warming: the rapid disintegration of Greenland's ice sheet. Such an event could indeed raise sea level more than 20 feet. However, multiple lines of evidence show this simply is not going to happen. Seventy percent of Greenland's ice sheet has in the past survived over 10 times as much heat as humans can possibly unload on it. The polar bear survived then; it will survive whatever we do to the atmosphere, too.

Despite the hurricane of self-congratulatory hoopla that accompanied the end of the Paris fetê, close analysis will reveal a climate agreement that will accomplish little while costing the United States and the European Union a lot. It is a lukewarm agreement, as befits a lukewarm world.

Readers may note the format of this book is a bit different from most popular science and policy texts. Rather than being composed of a dozen or so long chapters, it is broken into much smaller essays with topical titles. If the form looks familiar, you may be recalling Kurt Vonnegut's masterpiece *Cat's Cradle*, a wonderfully funny book about how government and science bring about the end of the world.[4]

Vonnegut delimited his short essays with a triangle of dots to reinforce his theme: that a new crystalline lattice structure for water—thanks to a special seeding nucleus—was about to kill everything on Earth. It looked like this: ∴.

---

[4] Kurt Vonnegut, *Cat's Cradle* (New York: Henry Holt, 1963).

The delimiters in this book consist of arrays of hurricane symbols. The number of symbols varies among chapters. The reader is left to decipher the code.

For what it's worth, Vonnegut's brother Bernard discovered cloud seeding, which uses a novel condensation nucleus—silver iodide—to cause moisture to condense into raindrops. So it goes.

An Important Note on Temperature Histories and Trends

The electronic version of this book, published in October 2015, used observed temperature records through 2014. They have been updated to encompass 2015, a year that saw a very strong El Niño event—a weakening or reversal of the trade winds over the tropical Pacific. El Niño, a quasi-periodic phenomenon, suppresses the normal upwelling of cold water off the west coast of South America and creates a temporary spike in global temperatures. This means our temperature records end with a very sharp uptick.

This has some effect on recent trends, including the infamous "pause" or "hiatus" in global warming during recent decades. However, it is important to note that when El Niños dissipate—something that is likely to happen in 2016—the suppressed cold upwelling returns and temperatures often drop to the same level (or even below) where they were prior to the El Niño, as happened following the 1998 event.

As of this writing in April 2016, temperatures have embarked upon a sharp decline. That said, annual temperatures in the later years of this decade (beginning in 2017) very likely will be considerably below their 2015 peak.

There also has been a partial revision of one of the two satellite datasets—that of Remote Sensing Systems as published in March 2016. We will note this in subsequent text. The dataset shows slightly warmer temperatures in recent years than did its predecessor. However, only the values for the midtroposphere (the bottom 40,000 feet of the atmosphere) have been published as of this writing. This is important because in this book we largely are interested in lower tropospheric temperatures because they are closer to the earth's surface.

Finally, our revisions to the 2015 electronic edition take note of a controversial adjustment in sea surface temperature data by the U.S. Department of Commerce that purports to get rid of "the pause" in global warming. It didn't (using normative scientific standards), but the adjustment subsequently was adopted by NASA and suddenly that agency's post-1998 data "warmed." The other temperature history we rely upon—from the Climate Research Unit at the University of East Anglia—also changed its temperature record by increasing its coverage of high northern latitudes and the Arctic Ocean. We comment on this revision later in our text. Suffice to say, we find it to be scientifically fanciful.

If you wonder why all of these governmental entities would suddenly revise their records to give an appearance of wiping away the "pause," we provide answers throughout this book. But, in a word, the answer is "Paris," a reference to the climate conference that took place in a suburb of the French capitol in December 2015.

1. A Little History

> When the search for truth is confused with political advocacy,
> the pursuit of knowledge is reduced to the quest for power.
>
> —Alston Chase*

In the minds of two powerful former U.S. senators—John Kerry (D-MA) and Tim Wirth (D-CO)—global warming science became political theater 27 years ago.

On a very hot June 23, 1988, at the height of a substantial drought over much of the nation and in the midst of a major eastern heatwave, a National Aeronautics and Space Administration (NASA) researcher, James Hansen, lit the bonfire of the greenhouse vanities. Hansen testified to the U.S. Senate Energy and Natural Resources Committee that there "is a strong cause and effect relationship . . . between the current climate and human alteration of the atmosphere." He presented a global temperature history derived from weather stations around the planet. It showed about 0.7°C (1.3°F) of warming in the previous 100 years, including warming in the decade prior to his testimony.[1, 2, 3]

Senator Wirth presided over the June 23 hearing. The room was very hot. Hansen repeatedly wiped his brow to absorb a sheen of perspiration along his receding hairline. Wirth was interviewed

---

* Alston Chase is an author and former philosophy professor with degrees from Harvard, Oxford, and Princeton universities. He is quoted by Michael Crichton in *State of Fear* (New York: HarperCollins, 2004; New York: Harper, 2009), p. 816. Citation refers to the 2009 paperback edition.

[1] The high temperature the day before the hearing remains the hottest June 22nd on record—101°F. The low temperature overnight was 76°F, still the record-warm low temperature for June 23. The high of 98°F on the day of Hansen's testimony remains a record, too.

[2] A bestselling novel at the time was Tom Wolfe's *Bonfire of the Vanities*, a story of New York decrepitude. Coincidentally, Dr. Hansen's lab was located above a diner on Broadway in New York named Tom's Restaurant.

[3] James E. Hansen, NASA Goddard Institute for Space Studies, testimony before the Senate Energy and Natural Resources Committee, 100th Cong., 2nd sess., June 23, 1988.

about the landmark hearing by PBS's *Frontline* on April 24, 2007, and admitted to disabling the room's air conditioning:

> What we did it [*sic*] was went in the night before and opened all the windows, I will admit, right? So that the air conditioning wasn't working inside the room and so when the, when the hearing occurred there was not only bliss, which is television cameras in double figures, but it was really hot.

> So Hansen's giving this testimony, you've got these television cameras back there heating up the room, and the air conditioning in the room didn't appear to work. So it was sort of a perfect collection of events that happened that day, with the wonderful Jim Hansen, who was wiping his brow at the witness table and giving this remarkable testimony.[4]

Senator Kerry wasn't there, but he told the Atlantic Council on March 12, 2015, "We heard Jim Hansen sit in front of us and tell us it's happening now, 1988." As chairman of the Senate Foreign Relations Committee, Kerry previously had opened a January 28, 2009, hearing and waxed historically, "On a sweltering June day, some Senate staff opened up the windows and drove home the point for everyone sweating in their seats during Dr. James Hansen's historic and tragically prescient testimony."

Both Wirth and Kerry are confabulating. Clearly they wanted to take some credit for the impact of Hansen's testimony, but when confronted with a statement provided to the *Washington Post*'s "The Fact Checker" by David Harwood—who was Wirth's chief of staff for climate change at the time—that "the windows being open absolutely did not happen," Wirth responded:

> Some myths about the hearing have also circulated over the years, including the idea that the windows were left open or the air conditioning was not working. While I've heard that version of events and repeated it myself, I've since learned it didn't happen.

Those myths were created by Wirth himself. The version of events was of his own making. He repeated it himself—in the first person—and yet knew it didn't happen because he'd made it up. This

---

[4] Sen. Tim Wirth, interview in "Hot Politics," *Frontline*, PBS, April 24, 2007. The actual chairman of the committee was Sen. J. Bennett Johnston (D–LA), but Wirth wielded the gavel for much of the hearing.

sad montage reveals that even decades ago the desire to turn global warming from science into theater was so strong that proponents imagined they were accomplishing it. Fewer than two months after the hearing, Wirth had explained the importance of his method of handling the issue in the August 13, 1988, edition of *National Journal*:

> What we've got to do in energy conservation is try to ride the global warming issue. Even if the theory of global warming is wrong, to have approached global warming as if it is real means energy conservation, so we will be doing the right thing anyway in terms of economic policy and environmental policy.

Hansen's stirring testimony was the lead story on network news. In a call-in poll two days later, CNN found that a vast majority of the respondents believed that the heat and drought were a result of carbon dioxide emissions. This probably was the first conflation of weather (a short-term phenomenon, like a heatwave) and global warming, which operates on the scale of decades. It certainly didn't prove to be the last time it would happen.

If there had been an Internet and social media at the time, Hansen could have taken credit for making global warming go viral. He would be "trending." After all, he had a temperature record showing that earth's surface was heating—fast.

Critics argued that some of the warming was due to the fact that cities have a way of growing up around their long-term weather stations, which usually are downtown. Frequently in the early 20th century, the official weather stations were moved to a new airport, initially out in the country but soon also to urbanize.

In March 1990, *Science*, the most prestigious academic science periodical in the Western Hemisphere, published a paper showing the first 11 years of temperature data derived from orbiting satellites. The two authors were NASA scientists Roy Spencer and John Christy at the agency's sprawling Huntsville, Alabama, research complex. Their brief record showed no warming whatsoever.

The satellites were sensing the vibration of atoms in the oxygen molecule (O_2). For a constellation of complicated reasons, the diatomic bond in this molecule vibrates in the microwave portion of the spectrum proportionate to its temperature. Just as the expansion of mercury in an evacuated column provides a proxy for heat (temperature), so does the vibration of oxygen.

The first satellite with a microwave sounding unit (MSU) became operational in late 1978. Its orbit was designed to pass over the same region of the Earth at the same time every day. The synchronicity is important, as temperatures in the layer that it senses (and hence the vibration of oxygen) are dependent upon the time of day. While that effect becomes attenuated a few thousand feet above Earth's surface, it is enough to require a carefully calibrated and monitored orbit.

Hansen's critics had a field day when Spencer and Christy's data showed no warming whatsoever. The MSU signal band they had chosen represents a vertical slice of the atmosphere roughly from 5,000 to 30,000 feet, with the signal maximizing around 10,000 feet. There are no cities there and no warming to be found.

Meanwhile, James Angel, an employee of the National Oceanic and Atmospheric Administration, began to compile data from twice-daily weather balloon launches. Instruments dangling from the balloon sense temperature using calibrated and standardized instrumentation. The balloon data are totally independent of the surface temperature record and of the satellite data. When Angel looked at balloon data from the atmospheric layer that corresponds to Spencer and Christy's, he couldn't find a lick of warming either.

So, by the early 1990s, three temperature measurements were available: surface thermometers, satellite MSUs, and weather balloons. The only one that could be biased by urban heating showed warming; the other two didn't.

In succeeding years, although Spencer and Christy's record continued to show no warming, Frank Wentz of Remote Sensing Systems (RSS)—a Santa Rosa, California, consultancy—demonstrated that the temperature-sensing satellites were experiencing a slight orbital decay that affected the data and effectively induced a slight cooling. When Wentz adjusted for this, the satellite data acquired a warming trend after all. Wentz, Spencer, and Christy traveled around the country in an endless round of panel discussions debating the validity of each other's approach. Spencer and Christy acknowledged Wentz's point about orbital decay and attempted their own adjustment. It, too, induced a warming trend—but one a wee bit less than that of Wentz. This time, global warming advocates were ecstatic. Finally the satellite data had been taken down! But in the critics' enthusiasm they failed to notice that the satellite warming was muted, running at about half of what computer models suggest. "Lukewarming" had begun.

Ironically, since January 1995 the RSS data show no statistically significant warming trend. (A warming trend may have been induced briefly by 2016's temporary El Niño spike.) Yet, even with that spike, there is no significant trend since June 1996 in Spencer's and Christy's data (as of this writing in April 2016). That was about the time Wentz went public with his first finding that there was a warming trend in Spencer and Christy's data. While the RSS data stopped warming, Spencer and Christy's complete record (1979–2016) does have an overall warming trend, albeit a small one. Recently, Spencer and Christy issued the latest iteration of their record, adjusting for some drifting instruments (among other things). Their record now has fallen into line with that of the RSS. Both data sets for the lower atmosphere are in their 19th year with no significant warming.

In March 2016, RSS updated its data but the results for the lower troposphere—the layer closest to the surface—were not available for analysis as of this writing. The overall trend in the midtropospheric data (which is higher and not as useful for comparison with the surface data) is not significantly different than that of Spencer and Christy, but the latter years are warmer. This revision does not match updated tropical weather balloon data as well as the UAH (University of Alabama in Huntsville) record does, so there may be unresolved problems with it.[5]

Around the year 2000, other teams of scientists began looking more in depth at the weather balloon data. It was discovered that the noise-to-signal ratio in some of the tropical data appeared to be far too large. When the bad tropical data were removed from the record, the weather balloon record in nearly the same slice of the atmosphere as that monitored by the satellite (roughly 5,000–30,000 feet elevation) also developed a slight warming. The match between the two records composes part of Figure 1 in the next chapter. Their comparison with forecast changes is decidedly lukewarm.

Summarizing: the lukewarm view of climate change arose from the refinement of climate records, all of which now are in agreement that while there has been a warming, it is far less than what was predicted to happen. Instead, temperature is lukewarming.

[5] Carl A. Mears and Frank J. Wentz. "Sensitivity of Satellite-Derived Tropospheric Temperature Trends to the Diurnal Cycle Adjustment." *Journal of Climate* (2016). doi:10.1175/jcli-d-15-0744.1.

2. The Lukewarm World

The threat is usually more terrifying than the thing itself.

—Saul Alinsky*

Who needs 1,000 words, when there's this picture (Figure 1)?

Figure 1

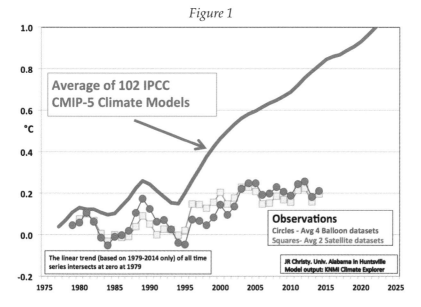

Note: Five-year running mean temperatures predicted by the UN Intergovernmental Panel on Climate Change's climate models and observed lower-atmospheric temperatures from weather balloons and satellites.[1]

---

* Saul Alinsky (1909–72) was an American community organizer and writer. The quotation is from Alinsky's *Rules for Radicals*, 1971.

[1] Adapted from John Christy, "CEQ Draft Guidance for GHG Emissions and the Effects of Climate Change," as contained in testimony presented to the U.S. House of Representatives Committee on Natural Resources oversight hearing on "The Obama Administration's CEQ Recently Revised Draft Guidance for GHG Emissions and the Effects of Climate Change," 114th Cong., 1st sess., May 13, 2015, http://naturalresources .house.gov/uploadedfiles/christytestimonyemr.pdf.

This graph was prepared by John Christy and Richard McNider at the University of Alabama. It was a part of Christy's testimony before the U.S. House Committee on Natural Resources on May 13, 2015. It, or something like it, is known to everyone involved in the discussion of global climate change.

The top line, trending ever upward (with the exception of slight cooling caused by volcanoes erupting in 1982 and 1991) is the five-year running average of global lower atmospheric temperature as predicted by the suite of 102 climate models used in the authoritative (which does not mean "correct") 2013 scientific assessment report by the UN Intergovernmental Panel on Climate Change (IPCC). The mean lower atmospheric warming predicted by the models for the satellite era is approximately 0.7°C (1.3°F).[2, 3, 4, 5]

The green squares represent global lower atmospheric temperature as measured by satellites. The data have been processed by two research teams. One is Spencer's and Christy's, the other is by Remote Sensing Systems. The two are ever-so-slightly different because they are not calibrated in the same way. The average of the two is shown. The warming observed by the satellites since 1979 is approximately 0.25°C (0.45°F).

The blue circles depict lower atmospheric temperatures as measured by weather balloons near the same altitude where the satellites sense temperature. There are four different analyses of this cumbersome dataset. The average of the four is shown. The warming observed by the weather balloons since 1979 is approximately 0.2°C. It's reassuring that the satellite and weather balloon data, being completely independent measurements, are so similar. Likewise, it is profoundly disturbing that the forecast is so far removed from reality.

There are two fits of declining temperatures. One in the early 1980s results from the eruption of El Chichón. The other is in the

---

[2] Technically, they are midtropospheric temperatures, roughly in the zone from 5,000–30,000 feet. These do not suffer from the confounding effects of urbanization or site changes.

[3] The IPCC fifth assessment report is a compilation of three volumes and a synthesis report prepared by the UN Intergovernmental Panel on Climate Change, 2014.

[4] Of the 108 models, 102 generate temperatures in this layer.

[5] Note that Christy's and McNider's model data plot extends to 2025. What we report are the 1979–2013 totals.

early 1990s when Mt. Pinatubo erupted with the biggest explosion on earth since Alaska's Katmai volcano in 1912. Both events are factored into the computer simulations, which is why they are captured both by the models and reality. But since Pinatubo there hasn't been a big blowup, so the atmosphere should be running free with global warming unfettered. It is obvious that the predicted rate of warming under undisturbed (nonvolcanic) conditions simply is too high. Why has our profession been so reluctant to admit the truth and say that it has made potentially the most costly and bad atmospheric forecast in human history? Maybe it's human nature to hold on to a bad forecast.

As of this writing in April 2016, the warmest year in the instrument record is 2015, in large part because of El Niño. The record reliably goes back to about 1900 (see the note on page xvii). To give an idea how badly the forecast is going—even if 2016 or 2017 turns out to be a record year—the disparity between the forecast and what is being observed will continue and, perhaps, even grow.[6]

The atmosphere isn't warming nearly as fast as is predicted in the forecasts that serve as the basis for some of the most onerous environmental regulations ever proposed (and adopted). In fact, you might say, instead of dramatic warming, lower atmospheric temperatures are lukewarming.

It took only 556 words and a picture to show this.[7]

---

[6] This is not unexpected. Because a slight warming pressure has been increasing in the atmosphere as the carbon dioxide concentration rises, a year (like 2015) in which there is an El Niño (a normal, somewhat periodic warming of the tropical Pacific Ocean) should set a record in the instrumental history.

[7] Note that we are not using surface temperatures for comparison. They are much more difficult to measure accurately and, as shown in Chapter 14, are subject to some very controversial adjustments that almost always yield more warming than is evident in the raw data.

3. Autumn in Paris

> The urge to save humanity is almost always only a false face
> to rule it.
>
> —H. L. Mencken

For global warming, 2015 was a big year. The biggest El Niño since 1998 spiked global surface temperatures to set a modern record. Both Pope Francis and President Obama agreed that climate change is the most important issue of our time. What could possibly prevent the world from agreeing to a new climate treaty to replace 1977's failed and expired Kyoto Protocol? The protocol had modified the United Nations' (UN) 1992 Framework Convention on Climate Change and, ultimately, had no detectable effect on atmospheric carbon dioxide levels.

Since 2009, the UN has been struggling to produce a new agreement. The Paris meeting was to be the 21st Conference of the Parties to the Framework Convention, or COP-21. Would environmentalists celebrate it as the meeting at which the entire world—rich and poor alike from Siberia to Cape Town and from Ushuaia to Resolute— finally agree to a global protocol to cut emissions of carbon dioxide?

Carbon dioxide represents the respiration of industrial civilization as powered by combustion of hydrocarbons such as coal, oil, and natural gas. Carbon dioxide emerges from the smokestacks of power plants, and the exhaust of automobiles and jet engines. A real, meaningful climate agreement only can succeed if the world literally changes and does so in ways that no one can comprehend. We simply don't know how to power or develop a modern economy either without emitting vast quantities of carbon dioxide and/or proliferating nuclear fusion worldwide, including regions occupied by hostile jihadists.

Would a celebration be warranted?

As will be shown later in this chapter, there were very few nations at COP-21 that agreed to do anything that differed from business-as-usual absent a climate accord. Few nations agreed to deviate significantly from their present path and incur substantial—and politically unpopular—costs. The agreement contains no legally-binding language able to compel any nation to reduce its emissions.

The Paris summiteers were determined not to repeat the failure of the previous UN attempt to comprehensively replace the Kyoto Protocol. That failure was at the 2009 meeting (COP-15) in Copenhagen. President Obama jetted in near the meeting's end, declared a climate victory, and hightailed it back to Washington in an effort to beat the first of three true blizzards that struck the Nation's Capitol that winter.[1] All that the delegates agreed to do was to send in a plan by February 2010 concerning how their country would reduce its emissions. A month later, UN climate chief Yvo de Boer announced even that wouldn't be necessary. He then up and quit.

At 2014's COP in Lima, Peru, everyone agreed to submit an Intended Nationally Determined Contribution (INDC) toward a global reduction in carbon dioxide emissions long *before* COP-21 convened in Paris. Because these were to be voluntary, each nation could "intend" to do as little as it might like—and that's what most did. All that was left to accomplish in Paris was implement the transfer of over $100 billion per year by 2020 to the developing world from the developed world (read that as the United States and European Union [EU]) into something called the "green climate fund." The funds are intended to compensate poorer nations for ostensible damages from developed world emissions and for investment in renewable energy sources such as solar and wind—sources that never will be able to provide sufficient and dependable juice to power any modern society.

President Obama loves the global warming issue. It provides him with power completely unmodulated by Congress. Thanks to the U.S. Supreme Court's 2007 decision in *Massachusetts v. Environmental Protection Agency*, the U.S. Environmental Protection Agency (EPA) is required to mandate substantial reductions in emissions of carbon dioxide if it "finds" that carbon dioxide—via climate change—endangers human health and welfare. EPA then must regulate it, presumably to the point that it no longer endangers. That's why EPA and the U.S. Department of Energy have gotten into the business

---

[1] Obama didn't make it. While Air Force One was able to make a perfectly safe landing in near-zero visibility at Andrews Air Force Base, it was far too dangerous to helicopter the president back to the White(out) House. So he arrived by motorcade during a howling blizzard.

of regulating dishwashers, washer/dryers, microwave ovens, motor vehicles, and power plants. Passenger aircraft are next.

None of this requires the approval of Congress, which waived its right to do so a long time ago when it passed the National Environmental Policy Act (NEPA) and President Richard Nixon signed it into law on New Year's Day, 1970.[2]

NEPA created a new bureaucracy—the President's Council on Environmental Quality—that lobbied Nixon to reshuffle some federal agencies and branches into a brand new agency for the protection of the environment. EPA's charter was intended to make it the focal point for issuance and coordination of environmental regulation. It would be answerable to the president, not Congress. As a result, the president can tell EPA—either explicitly or implicitly—what to do. That's how EPA was able to issue a preliminary "finding of endangerment" from carbon dioxide a mere 90 days into the new Obama administration. It issued its final finding on December 7, 2009 (Pearl Harbor Day) coincident with the kickoff of the failed Copenhagen climate summit.

Congress could, of course, tell EPA to cease and desist on carbon dioxide. But the president would immediately veto that. Still more ominously, it is unclear if the Supreme Court would even allow Congress to act in the context of its decision in *Massachusetts v. EPA*.[3]

In the run-up to the conference in Paris, EPA was fastly and furiously proposing or imposing carbon dioxide regulations. That's because the developing world, including the world's largest emitter (China), wouldn't agree to big-time emissions reductions unless the United States implemented them, too. Even then, there would be no guarantee.

---

[2] There is an exception. In 1994, Congress passed the Congressional Review Act as a part of the "Contract with America" championed by newly-elected House majority leader Newt Gingrich (R-GA). But use of that authority could be expected to be vetoed by a Democrat president.

[3] On February 9, 2016, the U.S. Supreme Court voted 5-4 to "stay" EPA's Clean Power Plan pending its review of a case contesting the plan's legality in 2017. While the court offered no specific reason for its stay, a year earlier the late Justice Antonin Scalia had written a majority opinion threatening a very close look at sweeping environmental regulations that lack specific assent by Congress. Under normal circumstances, this probably would have signaled the end of EPA's plan. But Scalia died four days later during a Texas hunting trip.

President Obama visited China in 2014, and on November 11, breathlessly announced a "historic agreement" in which China agreed, for the first time, to limit its emissions of carbon dioxide. Well, not really. China merely said it "intends" to hold its emissions constant sometime "around" 2030. The United States, on the other hand, is committed to a 26–28 percent reduction (from 2005 levels) by the end of 2025.

Think of this agreement in the context of a marriage proposal: "Honey, I intend to marry you around 15 years from now." How do you think that would work out? Notwithstanding the vague, non-committal language to which the Chinese agreed, President Obama brandished this "historic announcement" wherever he went in his campaign to arm-twist the developing world into agreeing to emissions reductions at COP-21. In January 2015, the president traveled to India to cajole Prime Minister Narendra Modi, who wouldn't even agree to "intend" to reduce emissions "around" any year.

An INDC's voluntary nature appears to elicit two kinds of responses. Some countries see INDCs as an opportunity to climb down from previously announced emissions reduction plans or commitments. A few others provide obviously outrageous ones they have no intention of fulfilling and can use to "chest thump" about their green virtue while soliciting funding from either the Obama or an Obama-like administration. Examples abound.

Russia's COP-21 proposal results in a more lax timetable for emissions reductions than Russia previously required of itself in its own binding domestic policy.

Look closely at Figure 2 and you'll notice Russia's goal is based on "maximum possible carbon dioxide" uptake by its forests rather than actual emissions reductions. Months before the Paris meeting, Russia's proposal already had the environmental community wringing its already wrung hands.

Figure 2

Russia's Submitted INDC

INDC	Limiting anthropogenic greenhouse gases in Russia to 70-75% of 1990 levels by the year 2030 might be a long-term indicator, subject to the maximum possible account of absorbing capacity of forests.
Planning processes and forecasts	The Russian Federation currently has in force legally-binding instruments aimed at providing for limitation of the GHG emissions to 70-75% of 1990 levels by the year 2020 (Decree of the President of the Russian Federation of 30 September 2013 and Act of the Government of the Russian Federation of 2 April 2014 No. 504-p). These acts provide for organization of GHG emissions forecasting at the economy-wide scale and for each individual sector. The Russian Federation will further elaborate and adopt legislative and regulatory acts providing for achievement of the stated INDC target by 2030 based on the provisions of the Climate Doctrine and the Energy Strategy of the Russian Federation.

Note: The top panel is from Russia's intended, nationally determined contribution for COP-21 and proposes a 70–75 percent reduction in its emissions by 2030. The previously published bottom panel states Russia's "legally-binding instruments" require a 70–75 percent reduction by 2020. In other words, what Russia sent to the UN slips its own legally binding commitment by 10 years, to 2030.[4]

Mexico took the opposite tack by intending the impossible. It claims its emissions will peak in 2026. That's 11 years from now and will be some neat trick considering these data in Figure 3:

[4] "Climate: Russia Sketches Emissions Cut of Up to 30%," *Economic Times*, April 1, 2015, http://economictimes.indiatimes.com/news/international/world-ws/climate-russia-sketches-emissions-cut-of-up-to-30/articleshow/46764115.cms.

Figure 3

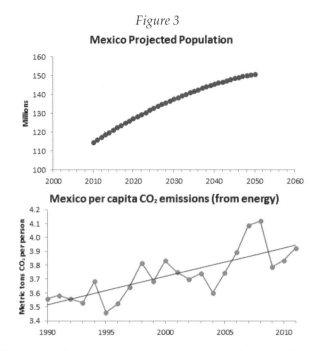

Mexico Projected Population

Mexico per capita CO₂ emissions (from energy)

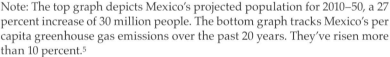

Note: The top graph depicts Mexico's projected population for 2010–50, a 27 percent increase of 30 million people. The bottom graph tracks Mexico's per capita greenhouse gas emissions over the past 20 years. They've risen more than 10 percent.[5]

Mexico's INDC will not only halt its growth in per capita emissions in just over a decade, but dial them downward in order to offset increased population. Because Mexico's per capita emissions are rising at 0.5 percent per year, its INDC would induce a sustained decline. The Obama administration waxed enthusiastic about Mexico's intent, yet the only way this can be more than an empty promise is for the Mexican government to drastically curtail per capita energy availability, a move that would be politically suicidal.

Then there's the United States. While our INDC is the largest on the planet in terms of absolute emissions reductions, it also represents a walking back of previous U.S. commitments.

[5] Mexico's population projections data are from the World Bank (http://datatopics.worldbank.org/hnp/popestimates). Per capita carbon dioxide emissions data are from the U.S. Energy Information Administration, International Energy Statistics (http://www.eia.gov/cfapps/ipdbproject/iedindex3.cfm?tid =90&pid=44&aid=8).

16

According to the Obama administration, "The United States intends to achieve an economy-wide target of reducing its greenhouse gas emissions by 26%–28% below its 2005 level in 2025 and to make best efforts to reduce its emissions by 28%." That's a bit less than the United States proposed to do in 2009 while negotiating at COP-15 in Copenhagen. At that time, the United States pledged a 30 percent reduction by 2025 and a 42 percent reduction by 2030. Our declining pledge probably is in deference to a thing called reality—as illustrated by Figure 4.

Figure 4

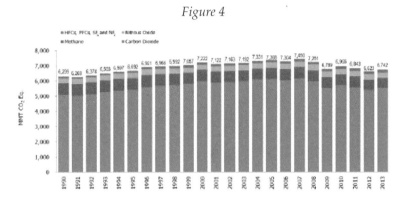

Note: U.S. greenhouse gas emissions by gas. Emissions values are presented in carbon dioxide equivalent mass units using the methodology of the UN's Intergovernmental Panel on Climate Change.[6]

As seen in Figure 4, at the time of the failed Copenhagen climate conference in 2009, U.S greenhouse gas emissions had been in fitful decline for about five years and stood 8 percent below 2005 levels. Between 2009–2013 (the span in EPA's figures), little had changed. Early indications are that 2014's emissions will be a bit higher than in 2013 even though natural gas has cut into coal's contribution toward electricity generation, trimming it from 44 percent to 39 percent. On its own, the switch from coal to gas would have reduced U.S. emissions some 1.6 percent.

But that cut doesn't translate economy-wide. Car sales increased as the economy slowly recovered. As they hit the roads, those cars

[6]U.S. Environmental Protection Agency, *Inventory of U.S. Greenhouse Gas Emissions and Sinks: Report, 1990–2013* (Washington, D.C.: EPA, 2015), http://www.epa.gov /climatechange/ghgemissions/usinventoryreport.html.

added more emissions. This shows why it is so hard to enjoy economic growth and reductions in carbon dioxide at the same time.

In any case, all of this pregame activity signaled that whatever was to emerge from the Paris conference likely would be pretty lukewarm, despite an expected proclamation of success.

The failure at Copenhagen in 2009 had been made worse by the fact that presidents and prime ministers didn't show up until near its end. This gave the appearance of them presiding over a diplomatic catastrophe. When President Obama arrived at a meeting of the BRICs (Brazil, Russia, India, and China), he was all chummy and wanted an open chat. His entourage gently was shown the door. By contrast, at the Paris conference, President Obama and Pope Francis's secretary of state, Cardinal Pietro Parolin, both spoke on the opening day of COP-21. Success was assured, right?

First, advance teams of mid-level bureaucrats arrived. After opening ceremonies that resembled an Olympiad hosted by a totalitarian regime, world leaders—including Obama—gave speeches and press conferences. Developing country heads-of-state or their deputies announced all kinds of good intentions before getting down to panhandling the developed nations (mainly the United States and EU). After about a week, the press pronounced the meeting "hopelessly deadlocked" over funding for developing nations. The hopeless deadlock required an extension of COP-21 beyond its Friday, December 11, closing date. Within 24 hours a "breakthrough" was announced and, as in Copenhagen in 2009, victory was declared.

The Paris Agreement, as it is called, is climatically inconsequential and completely unenforceable. Therefore it is a lukewarm agreement. This book may convince you that this is not a bad outcome—except for the United States and European Union. Lukewarm climate change is consistent with lukewarm policy.

❞❞❞

4. Getting Real about the Greenhouse Effect

There is no longer any significant disagreement in the scientific community that the greenhouse effect is real and already occurring.

—U.S. Sen. Al Gore (1986)

The hotter an object is, the more it radiates in the energetic, shorter wavelengths of the electromagnetic spectrum. Because the sun's surface is about 5,500°C (9,930°F), it emits maximally smack in the middle of the visible spectrum. The Earth's surface averages a piddling 15°C (59°F) and the planet radiates outward much longer wavelengths, maximizing in the longwave infrared far beyond a rainbow's red end.

In fact, about the only things that get excited about the infrared radiation emanating from our planetary surface are two atmospheric gases: water vapor and carbon dioxide. Both are shaped in such a way that when a unit of infrared strikes them, they get turned on (the technical term is that they reach an "excited state"). Molecules of these greenhouse gases temporarily trap the infrared energy before detumescing and releasing it.

The individual packet of infrared energy being reradiated by a greenhouse gas either can go up—or out into space, where it was headed before it hit the molecule—or can go back down. If it goes downward, it will provide additional warming to the lower atmosphere and—if you're paying attention—there will be less energy available to warm the higher levels of the atmosphere, so they should cool. The transition between warming and cooling takes place at about 50,000 feet, where the turbulent troposphere (*tropo* meaning motion) gives way to the placid stratosphere.

Without the greenhouse gases (mainly water vapor), our planet's surface would be a lot colder than it is. Assuming that some water existed in small lakes or oceans, it would be frozen. Under such circumstances, it's doubtful evolution would have progressed much beyond various reproducing slimes. Greenhouse gases have done us a solid.

The key to understanding greenhouse warming—as opposed to a general warming caused by a hotter sun—is recognizing that increasing carbon dioxide or water vapor concentrations do not warm the earth-atmosphere system as a whole. Surface and lower atmospheric warming is balanced by a cooling at higher altitudes. There aren't a lot of other phenomena that result in a constantly changing differential between surface and stratospheric temperatures.

Lukewarmers know that the greenhouse effect is real and that increasing concentrations of greenhouse gases will change the climate.

5. Human Nature and Forecasting Models

Making a forecast is easy. Being right is the hard part.

—Reid A. Bryson*

A computer model is a string of computer code that tells electrons exactly what to do. Some are very useful, such as those used for weather forecasting.

Twice a day, technicians around the world simultaneously launch equipment-laden, helium-filled balloons to capture the three-dimensional structure of the atmosphere. It's surprisingly simple. Equipment in the sensor pod measures temperature, atmospheric pressure, and dew point. Dew point is the temperature at which moisture in the surrounding environment will condense (think of your lawn on a summer evening). Other technology detects position and change-of-position, which is a measure of the wind.

The vertical and horizontal distribution of these quantities is all that is required to run a weather forecasting model. But different models can give different results. For example, a week in advance, the model used by the European Center for Medium-Range Weather Forecasts predicted that 2012's Hurricane Sandy would turn inland and obliterate the North Jersey shore, while the American Global Forecast System (GFS) model predicted it would run harmlessly out to sea.[1]

A recent example shows how hard it can be to back down from a disaster forecast.

On January 26, 2015, the GFS predicted a major blizzard in an area from south of Philadelphia, Pennsylvania, all the way to Boston, Massachusetts. By early evening—with only a couple of inches of snow on the ground—skies cleared over Philadelphia and the heavy snow rapidly retreated to the northeast. Yet the National Weather

---

* Reid A. Bryson (1920–2008) was an American atmospheric scientist, geologist, and meteorologist. He was professor emeritus at the University of Wisconsin–Madison.

[1] By the time Hurricane Sandy made landfall, it no longer was a tropical cyclone.

Service's Philadelphia office held on to the earlier forecast long into the night, even as the clouds parted. The fact is that it is very hard to back down from a forecast of gloom and doom, especially one that provokes a massive public response—whether it is closing the New York City subway (as Gov. Andrew Cuomo ordered) or closing down coal-fired power plants because of a forecast of global warming disaster.

Climate models are similar to weather models, but with a twist. Instead of being updated every 12 hours using a revised snapshot of the atmosphere, they are "initialized" with a typical atmosphere and ocean. Then, instead of time-stepping every hour through a 16-day cycle, they move forward day by theoretical day 100 years into the future. The weather within the model is modulated only by a steady, but slowly increasing, lower atmospheric warming pressure from increasing carbon dioxide and by a goofy "aerosol" to keep the models from getting too hot (more on that later) because more and more of the radiation the Earth eventually emits out to space is recycled in the lower atmosphere before exiting—which is what happens as atmospheric carbon dioxide increases.

But how much does the incremental increase in downwelling radiation caused by increasing atmospheric carbon dioxide change the average surface temperature? The answer is complicated.

Earth's surface temperatures are highly dependent on local conditions. Black soil, like black clothing, will absorb a lot of radiation and heat up sharply. It is a common mistake to say that white surfaces *reflect* more radiation. Actually white snow will *absorb* very little radiation and warm a lot less. And what about the ocean? How much does an ocean surface warm and how much of that warming is transported downward to virtually disappear in its vast depths?

As a consequence, there are dozens of different climate models and each can be run in different ways. Some may handle clouds differently; others may incorporate large cooling parameters if, for other reasons, they tend to predict too much warming.[2]

There's also a human element. Suppose—thanks to public concern about dread global warming—Congress was to appropriate a fair amount of money for you to run your 100-year model. As

---

[2] The UN Intergovernmental Panel on Climate Change uses a total of 108 different model "runs."

anyone who has worked with these models knows, they incorporate "knobs" that can be adjusted to dramatically affect their predictions. If you set your model to predict not much warming, the issue goes away. Because there's an inherent interest in the workings of climate, your model will continue to be funded as a research tool. However, the massive scientific infrastructure that accompanies scary climate change wouldn't exist.

But do the opposite; adjust your model so the predicted warming is substantial. Could it be enough to cause Greenland to quickly shed all its ice and raise sea level 23 feet in 100 years, thereby drowning the urban core of many coastal cities? The damage would be spectacular! Most of it would occur quite suddenly, often during hurricanes or strong conventional cyclones. A high-end forecast like that could beget an entire industry of climatologists, ecologists, hydrologists, lobbyists, and nerds. Together, they might compose something like the U.S. Global Change Research Program, engaged in the normal political activity of such groups (i.e., looking out for their own self-interest).[3, 4]

Lukewarmers believe the most internally consistent synthesis of observed versus modeled temperatures points toward a low-end warming. In a lukewarm world, many climate scientists would move on to whatever the next problem might be—or they might start a consulting company, drive a cab, or join a Washington think tank.[5]

Lukewarmers recognize that scientists are human beings. While initially modeling a climate highly sensitive to greenhouse gases is human nature, the consequence is to distort the policy response to global warming.

[3] James E. Hansen, "Brief for Amicus Curiae, Dr. James Hansen," *Alec L. v. Jackson*, United States District Court for the Northern District of California–San Francisco Division, 2011, p. 8.

[4] As established by the U.S. Global Change Research Act of 1990, U.S.C. §§ 2921 (1990).

[5] These observations are based on the authors' personal experiences.

6. Grand Narratives, Availability Cascades, and Granfalloons

> If you wish to study a granfalloon, just remove the skin of a toy balloon.
>
> —*Books of Bokonon**

How might an issue like climate change, acid rain 30 years ago, or ocean acidification 10 years from now suddenly become the root cause of just about everything? How might they become what the Georgia Institute of Technology's Judy Curry calls "a grand narrative"?[1]

Consider just a few objects of the global warming grand narrative, many of which are touched upon in this book: war, poverty, disease, mental illness, cold winters, warm winters, sex, infertility, and [droning] on and on. Everything that goes wrong is used to reinforce the conviction that there is only one thing we can do to prevent such societal problems—stop burning fossil fuels. This grand narrative misleads us into thinking that if we solve the problem of climate change, then these other problems also will be solved.[2]

Politicians, activists, and journalists have stimulated an "availability cascade" to support alarm about human-caused climate change. An availability cascade is a self-reinforcing process of collective belief formation that triggers a self-perpetuating chain reaction: the more attention a particular danger receives, the more worried people become, which leads to more news coverage and increased alarm. Because slowly increasing temperatures don't seem particularly alarming, "availability entrepreneurs" promote

---

* The *Books of Bokonon* are the sacred texts of Bokonism, a fictional religion created by Kurt Vonnegut in writing *Cat's Cradle* (New York: Henry Holt, 1963).

[1] Much of this chapter is taken from Judith Curry's blog, *Climate Etc.*, in a fine post dated April 9, 2015, and called "Climate Change Availability." See http://judithcurry.com /2015/04/09/climate-change-availability-cascade.

[2] Ibid.

extreme weather events and their public health impacts as having been caused by human-caused climate change, more of which is in store if society doesn't quickly act to cool the planet by reducing fossil fuel emissions.[3, 4]

Availability cascades are classic granfalloons. Kurt Vonnegut defines "granfalloons" as "large but meaningless associations of human beings" in his classic, *Cat's Cradle*. The characteristic of a granfalloon is opposite that of a "karass" (meaningful association) in that everyone in a granfalloon believes in its deepest meaning. By way of example, the mendacious conflation of human-caused climate change with savage beheadings by ISIS in Syria and elsewhere is representative of a granfalloon belief system. So is the it's-worse-than-we-thought chant wrongly applied to sea-level rise, depleting food supplies, or mental illness.

A deconstruction of this particular availability cascade is necessary to avoid bias in our thinking and to better understand the true risks of human-caused climate change.[5]

The basis of the climate change availability cascade originates with the UN Framework Convention on Climate Change, adopted in June 1992. It's important to note that it wasn't until 1995 that the Intergovernmental Panel on Climate Change (IPCC) Second Assessment Report identified a "discernible human influence" on global climate.[6]

The Framework Convention changed the definition of climate change to refer to a change of climate that is attributed directly or indirectly to human activity. This leads to the perception that all climate change is caused by humans.[7]

---

[3] Timur Kuran and Cass R. Sunstein, "Availability Cascades and Risk Regulation," *Stanford Law Review* 51 (1999): 683–768.

[4] Curry, "Climate Change Availability."

[5] Ibid.

[6] Ibid. It's important to note, however, that the inclusion of the words "discernible human influence" was highly controversial because they were inserted into the IPCC's 1995 compendium by Benjamin Santer after the peer-review process had concluded—probably because it is highly doubtful they could have survived peer review.

[7] Ibid.

Sea-level rise and extreme weather events such as hurricanes, drought, and heat waves are attributed to climate change, which is de facto assumed to be human-caused climate change.[8]

Human health impacts, national security risks, and so on, are exacerbated by extreme weather events and likewise inferred to be caused by human-caused climate change.[9]

A critical linkage in this cascade is that of human-caused climate change and extreme weather. In 2012, the IPCC published a "Special Report on Managing the Risks of Extreme Events and Disasters to Advance Climate Change Adaptation." As Roger Pielke Jr. and others have repeatedly shown, there is no increasing trend in extreme weather and climate-related damages after one (necessarily) accounts for changes in population and property values. The report found low to medium confidence of a trend in droughts in some regions and the frequency of heavy rains in some regions, and high confidence of a trend in heat waves in Australia. There was no trend in hurricanes or wild fires. However, attribution of *any* trend in extreme weather events to human-caused climate change cannot be done with confidence. What we have, in general, are more people with more stuff living in harm's way, not more bad weather.[10, 11]

As a specific example of this cascade, consider a recent announcement by the White House that it will begin an initiative to focus on the health effects of climate change using a new draft report from the U.S. Global Change Research Program.[12]

Several years ago, several of us at Cato Institute addressed this issue with an impact assessment of climate change on the United States. We found that the health effects of climate change on the U.S. population are negligible and are likely to remain so. Forty-six percent of all U.S. deaths directly attributable to weather events from 1993 to 2006 were caused by excessive cold; 28 percent were from

---

[8] Ibid.

[9] Ibid.

[10] Ibid.

[11] CSPAN, "Testimony of Roger Pielke Jr. before the Senate Environment and Public Works Committee hearing on climate change, July 18, 2013," posted on YouTube, July 21, 2013, http://www.youtube.com/watch?v=meoETyMA4K0.

[12] U.S. Global Change Research Program, *The Impacts of Climate Change on Human Health in the United States: A Scientific Assessment*, last modified April 7, 2015, http://www.globalchange.gov/health-assessment.

excessive heat. We found that overall deaths from extreme weather events have declined in the United States. We also found that diseases transmitted by food, water, and insects have been reduced by orders of magnitude over the past century and show no sign of resurgence.[13, 14]

Regarding asthma (an issue that influences President Obama), the argument is that increasing heat waves will exacerbate smog, which will exacerbate the incidence of asthma. However, according to EPA, smog levels have declined 33 percent since 1980. Furthermore, the incidence of U.S. heat waves is not unprecedented. EPA's analysis of the U.S. heat wave index shows that during the 1930s the index reached levels almost an order of magnitude greater than those in the recent decade. While asthma rates have been climbing, the cause cannot be global warming as caused by humans. Nevertheless, a recent survey of American Thoracic Society members found that 77 percent of the respondents observed an impact from climate change on increased chronic disease severity from air pollution.[15, 16, 17]

An availability cascade that entices us to believe climate change is exacerbating chronic respiratory diseases such as asthma leads us away from a deeper investigation of the true cause of public health problems and from our addressing them in a meaningful way. Multiply that consequence across the entire range of issues in which climate change is alleged to be making things worse. The climate change availability cascade of apocalypse narrows our perspective and policy options that are necessary for dealing with complex issues such as public health, weather disasters, and national security. Should we be surprised when reducing carbon dioxide emissions doesn't actually ameliorate any of these problems?[18]

Is climate change making us stupid? Judith Curry fears the answer is yes. The problem is exacerbated by a politically correct climate change orthodoxy enforced by politicians, advocates, and the media

---

[13] Patrick Michaels et al., *ADDENDUM: Global Climate Change Impacts in the United States.* (Washington, D.C.: Cato Institute Center for the Study of Science, 2012).

[14] Curry, "Climate Change Availability."

[15] Michaels et al., *ADDENDUM*, p. 144.

[16] See Chapter 25, "Is Global Warming Making Us Ill?"

[17] Curry, "Climate Change Availability."

[18] Ibid.

in an availability cascade that is destroying our ability to think rationally about how we should respond to climate change.[19]

The result is an intense clamor for policy responses advocated by an activist community armed with the availability cascade. Scientists who stand in its way are disregarded as impediments to planetary salvation. After all, there are all too many research dollars available to those willing to add more water to the cataract.

The notion of an availability cascade related to climate science and policy is an exceedingly powerful paradigm, and we hope that readers keep it in mind as they progress through this volume.

---

[19] Ibid.

7. In the Availability Cascade, What Is Not Real Is Real

Facts are stubborn, but statistics are more pliable.

—Mark Twain

Recall Judith Curry's definition of an availability cascade as a self-reinforcing process of collective belief formation that triggers a self-perpetuating chain reaction. The more attention a danger gets, the more worried people become, leading to more news coverage and greater alarm.

We saw a classic self-reinforcing process of collective belief formation in May 2015. It began when Christopher Watson of the University of Tasmania published "Unabated Global Mean Sea-Level Rise over the Satellite Altimeter Era" in the May 11 edition of *Nature Climate Change*.[1]

What Watson and his team did was to correct satellite-sensed mean global sea-level, taking into account the fact that the sensors drift and correcting for land movements with sensitive GPS data applied to land-based tide gauges. So far, so reasonable. They wrote, "Our corrected GMSL [global mean sea-level] data indicate an acceleration in [the rate of] sea-level rise [based upon two different but related methodologies], which is of opposite sign to previous estimates."

Only in the world of the availability cascade would this data warrant publication. Prior to the team's study, the acceleration rate was given as −0.57 +/− 0.58 millimeters per year squared (rate changes are measured in terms of squared time units). The negative sign preceding the acceleration estimates actually means the rate of sea-level rise is *decelerating*. The "+/−" isn't even the usual 95 percent confidence limit. Rather, it represents one standard deviation, or a much more lax 67 percent confidence limit. So within this outrageously

---

[1] Christopher S. Watson et al., "Unabated Global Mean Sea-Level Rise over the Satellite Altimeter Era," *Nature Climate Change* 5 (2015): 565–68.

loose criterion, the acceleration (rather, deceleration) in sea-level rise from when the satellite data began in 1993 to the present is not distinguishable from zero—a fact curiously ignored by the press. After applying the correction to the satellite data with the GPS data, the authors report the deceleration turns into an acceleration of 0.41 +/– 0.58 mm/year[2], a value also easily encompassing zero.[2]

It gets better.

Prior to the adjustment made by Watson's team, the mean, satellite-sensed, sea-level rise was 3.2 +/– 0.4 mm/year (or a central value of a bit over one-tenth inch per year). Table 1 shows how these measurements stack up.

Table 1

Sea-level rise	Value	Range (one standard deviation)
Previous estimate	3.2 +/– 0.4 mm/yr	2.8–3.6 mm/yr
Watson method 1	2.6 +/– 0.4 mm/yr	2.2–3.2 mm/yr
Watson method 2	2.9 +/– 0.4 mm/yr	2.5–3.3 mm/yr

Only members of a granfalloon could possibly believe these data are statistically distinguishable one from another. But that didn't stop the researchers. They went on to write, regarding the acceleration figures, "Neither of these is significantly different from zero; however, the revised estimate is significantly different from the earlier estimate derived from data unadjusted for the effects of bias drift." No, it isn't, as you can see for yourself.

So the big story—the one that should have received a lot of attention—was that the rate of sea-level rise has remained constant over the satellite era. Instead, the reportage in *Science* contributes to the availability cascade.

Science reporter Julia Rosen wrote that the paper showed sea-levels "gaining ground faster than ever." We draw Table 1 to her attention. Even so, according to Rosen, "The result won't come as a shock to most climate scientists. Long-term records from coastal tide gauges have shown that sea-level rise accelerated throughout the 20th century."[3]

---

[2] Yes, the central value is negative, not positive.

[3] Julia Rosen, "Sea-level Rise Accelerating Faster Than Thought," *Science*, May 11, 2015, http://sciencemag.org/news/2015/05/sea-level-rise-accelerating-faster-thought.

Maybe not, as Figure 5 shows:

Figure 5

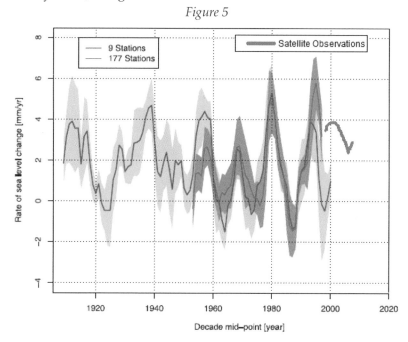

Note: Decadal rate of sea-level rise (1993–2015) from satellites (red curve) appended to the decadal rate of global sea-level rise as determined from a 9-station tide gauge network for the period 1904–2003 (blue curve) and from a 177-station tide gauge network for the period 1948–2002 (magenta). All data are 10-year running means.[4]

---

[4] S. J. Holgate, "On the Decadal Rates of Sea-Level Change During the 20th Century," *Geophysical Research Letters* 34 (2007): L01602. The figure includes additional satellite-derived sea-level data included from the website *CU Sea level Research Group*, University of Colorado, http://sealevel.colorado.edu.

Or, maybe—but not very much, as Figure 6 shows:

Figure 6

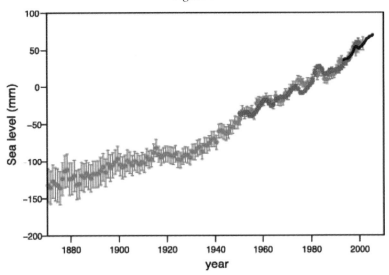

Note: A different analysis of tide-gauge data (with satellite data at the end) shows a very slight acceleration in sea-level rise in the past 50 years, concurrent with the era of anthropogenerated (human caused) climate change.[5]

John Church, one of Watson's coauthors, told *Science*, "Sea levels are rising at ever increasing rates, and society needs to take notice." That conclusion is not at all supported by the data within his own paper.

As noted by David Whitehouse of the Global Warming Policy Foundation on May 15, 2015:

> Not that the media noticed scientific details such as the flimsy base for claiming an acceleration in sea-level rise. The vast majority headlined it without any qualification. It is a clear

[5] James R. Houston and R. G. Dean, "Sea-Level Acceleration Based on U.S. Tide Gauges and Extensions of Previous Global-Gauge Analyses," *Journal of Coastal Research* 27 (2011): 409–17.

case of widespread poor science reporting. No financial journalist would not look at the figures behind a headline. Very few covering climate science ever do, and many would not even think to ask! It is yet another mismatch between what many in the media report, and what is in the peer-reviewed literature.[6]

[6] David Whitehouse, "The Sea-Level Acceleration Trap," from the Global Warming Policy Forum website, May 13, 2015, http://www.thegwpf.com/the-sea -level-acceleration-trap.

8. The Availability Cascade Runs Amok

United Nations Secretary General Ban Ki-moon said this year that global warming poses as much of a threat to the world as war.

—BBC (2007)

The availability cascade and its grand narratives sometimes have major international implications. For example, did global warming cause the current war in Syria, which would mean it also causes wanton decapitation? From mainstream press headlines, one would almost certainly think so.[1]

Reading more deeply into the articles in which this case is laid out, one notices that a few caveats appear. But, initially, the chain of events seems strong.

Here's the mechanism. According to Colin Kelley at the University of California–Santa Barbara, an extreme drought in the Fertile Crescent region was worsened by human greenhouse gas emissions. It added a critical spark to the tinderbox of tensions that had been amassing in Syria for a number of years under policies of Bashar al-Assad's regime (including very poor water management policies).[2]

However, it is not until one digs more deeply into the technical scientific literature that one sees that the anthropogenic climate change impact on drought conditions in the Fertile Crescent is both extremely minimal and tenuous—so much so that it is debatable whether it can be detected at all.

---

[1] "Syria's Civil War 'Linked to Global Warming,'" *Telegraph* (London), March 3, 2015, http://www.telegraph.co.uk/news/worldnews/middleeast/syria/11446093/Syrias-civil-war-linked-to-global-warming.html.

[2] Colin P. Kelley et al., "Climate Change in the Fertile Crescent and Implications of the Recent Syrian Drought," *Proceedings of the National Academy of Sciences* 112 (2015): 3241–46.

This is not to say that a strong and prolonged drought didn't play a role in Syria's prewar unrest. Perhaps it did; perhaps it didn't. That's a debate we'll leave to folks more qualified to judge than we are. But the impact of human-influenced climate change on the region's drought conditions was almost certainly too small to have mattered. The violence would almost certainly have occurred in any case.

It is true that climate models project a general drying trend throughout the Mediterranean region—including the area of the Fertile Crescent in the eastern Mediterranean. As the climate warms under increasing greenhouse gas concentrations, there are two components. One is a northward expansion of the subtropical high-pressure system that typically dominates the southern portion of the region. This poleward expansion of the high-pressure system would act to shunt wintertime storm systems northward, with the result of increasing precipitation over Europe while decreasing it across the Mediterranean region. The second component is an increase in temperature that would lead to increased evaporation and enhanced drying.

A graph in the headline-generating paper by Kelley and his team shows the observed trend in the sea-level pressure across the eastern Mediterranean as well as the trend projected to have taken place there by a collection of climate models.

Figure 7

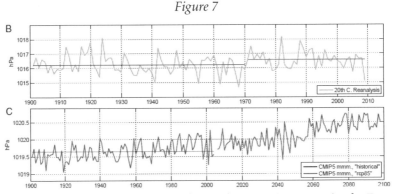

Note: Observed (top) and modeled (bottom) sea-level pressure for the Eastern Mediterranean region.[3]

---

[3] Ibid.

The connection between this drought and human-induced climate change is tenuous at best, and tendentious at worst.

If the subtropical high is expanding northward over the region, the observed sea-level pressure ought to be rising. Indeed, the climate models project (as shown in the bottom panel of Figure 7) a rise in the surface pressure over the 20th century (the blue portion of the curve) and an even greater rise into the future (the red portion). However, observations (the green line in the top panel) don't corroborate the modeled hypothesis under the normative rules of science. If one ignores the confusing horizontal lines inserted by the authors in an effort to convince you that what is *not* true is true, several problems that are characteristic of availability cascades become obvious. First, the level of natural variability is such that no overall trend is readily apparent.

The authors identify the upward trend as being "marginally significant (P < 0.14)." In reality, in no one's statistics book (except, perhaps, that of the authors) would a *P*-value of 0.14 be marginally significant. It is widely accepted throughout the scientific literature that P-values must be less than 0.05 for them to be considered statistically significant—in other words, the odds are less than 1 in 20 that chance alone would produce a similar result. That's normative science.

We've seen some rather rare cases in which authors attach the term "marginally significant" to *P*-values of up to 0.10, but 0.14 (about 1-in-7 odds that chance didn't produce it) is taking things a bit far. This is the basis for our earlier use of the word "tendentious" in describing the alleged connection between this drought and human-induced climate change.

Whether or not there is an identifiable overall upward trend, barometric pressure in the region during the last decade of the record (as the Syrian drought was taking place) is not at all unusual when compared with other periods in the region's pressure history—including periods that took place long before large-scale greenhouse gas emissions. Consequently, there is little in the pressure record that lends credence to the notion that human-induced climate change played a significant role in the region's recent drought.

Another clue that the human impact on the recent drought could have been no more than minimal comes from a 2012 paper in the *Journal of Climate* by Martin Hoerling and his colleagues. They conclude that about half of the trend toward late-20th-century dry conditions in the Mediterranean region is potentially attributable to human emissions of greenhouse gases and aerosols.

Climate models run with increasing concentrations of greenhouse gases and aerosols produce general drying across the Mediterranean region. However, the subregional patterns of the drying are sensitive to patterns of sea-surface temperature (SST) variability and change. Alas, the pattern of changes in SST is quite different than projected by the climate models. Hoerling's team describes the differences this way: "In general, the observed SST differences have stronger meridional [North–South] contrast between the tropics and NH [Northern Hemisphere] extra-tropics and also a stronger zonal [East–West] contrast between the Indian Ocean and the tropical Pacific Ocean."[4]

Depicted in Figure 8 is what Hoerling is describing—the observed SST change (top) along with the changes projected by the models (bottom) for the period 1971–2010, minus 1902–70. Note the complexity that accompanies reality.

What Hoerling's study shows is that—in the Fertile Crescent region—the drying produced by climate models is particularly enhanced (by some two to three times) if the observed patterns of sea-surface temperature are incorporated into the models rather than the patterns that would otherwise be projected by the models, meaning the top portion of Figure 8 is used to drive the model output and not the bottom portion.

Let's be clear. The models were unable to accurately reproduce the patterns of sea-surface temperature observed as greenhouse gas concentrations increased. So observed data were "prescribed" in place of the predicted value. The substitute data then were used to generate forecasts for changes in rainfall. We can't emphasize this enough: a reality that was *not forecast* by the climate models to happen as a consequence of climate change was forced into the models to synthesize rainfall.

Figures 9 and 10 show what the forecast was to have been and what actually was observed. Note that even using the "prescribed" (more accurately, fudged) substitute sea-surface temperatures, the precipitation changes predicted by the model (in the lower panel of Figure 9) only are about half as great as actually observed to have taken place in the region around Syria (Figure 10—note the difference in scale). As a consequence, the other half of the moisture de-

---

[4] Martin Hoerling et al., "On the Increased Frequency of Mediterranean Drought," *Journal of Climate* 25 (2012): 2146–61.

Figure 8

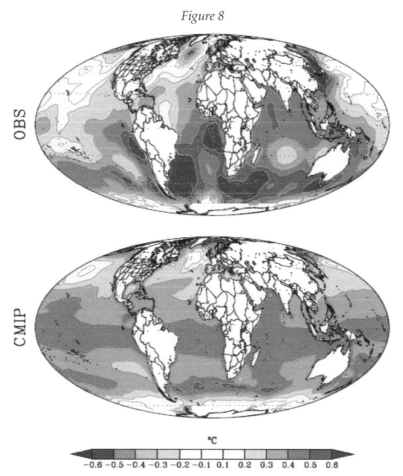

Note: November–April sea-surface temperature (°C) departures for the period 1971–2010 minus 1902–70; (top) observed and (bottom) mean from climate model projections.[5]

cline remains largely unexplained. In the top panel of Figure 9, you also can see that only about 10 mm out of the more than 60 mm of observed precipitation decline around Syria during the cold season is consistent with human-caused climate change as predicted by climate models when left to their own devices. "Consistent with" does not mean "caused by."

[5] Ibid.

Figure 9

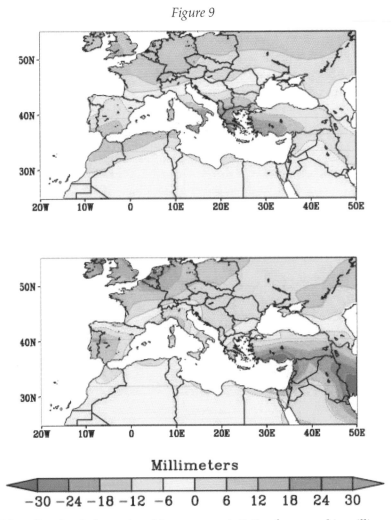

Note: Simulated change in cold-season precipitation (measured in millimeters) over the Mediterranean region based on the ensemble average of 22 IPCC models run with observed emissions of greenhouse gases and aerosols (top graph) and of 40 models run with observed emissions of greenhouse gases and aerosols along with prescribed (substituted) sea-surface temperatures (bottom graph). The different plots in the panels are for 1971–2010 minus 1902–70.[6]

[6] Ibid.

For the purpose of comparison, according to the climate history prepared by the University of East Anglia, average cold season rainfall in Syria is 261 mm (10.28 inches). Climate models, when left to their own devices, predict a decline in rainfall averaging about 10 mm—or 3.8 percent of the total. When the prescribed (or fudged) sea-surface temperatures are substituted, the decline in rainfall increases to 24 mm (or a bit less than an inch). That's 9.1 percent of the total. Meanwhile, the population that depends upon that rainfall roughly tripled in the past 30 years.

So which is creating the greater problem: a 10 percent reduction in rainfall (less than half of which can be tied to global warming) or a 300 percent increase in the number of people who rely upon it?

Figure 10

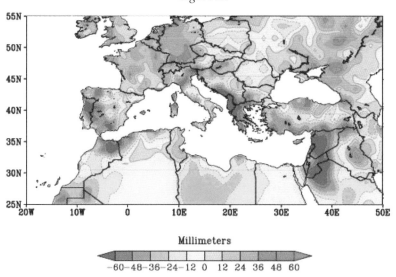

Note: Observed change in cold season precipitation for the period 1971–2010 minus 1902–70. Anomalies, as measured in millimeters, are relative to 1902–2010.[7]

After carefully comparing the patterns of observed changes in the meteorology and climatology of Syria and the Fertile Crescent with those produced by climate models, it is clear the lion's share of observed changes are unexplained by the models that are run with

[7] Ibid.

increasing greenhouse gases. Lacking a better explanation, these unexplained changes get chalked up to natural variability. As a consequence, it isn't climate but natural variability that dominated the region's observed climate history as it plunged into yet another war.

That is not what one would conclude if relying upon the cursory treatment of this paper as reported in the mainstream press. An in-depth analysis requires an examination of scientific literature, and a good background in and understanding of the rather technical research discussed in the paper.

Like all issues related to climate change, the devil is in the details. In the reporter's haste to produce attention-grabbing headlines, the details often are glossed over or dismissed. And that's what one can expect will happen in the presence of an availability cascade. All kinds of things (including wars and drought) get shoved into a single box labeled "global warming."

The identifiable influence of human-caused climate change on recent drought conditions in the Fertile Crescent hardly can be the straw that broke that camel's back and triggered the outbreak of conflict in Syria. The region's political climate seems plenty hot enough to ignite it. Recent drought conditions, which are part and parcel of the region's climate and largely are modulated by natural variability, could, at best, be a contributing factor—even in an era of increasing greenhouse gas emissions from human activities.

Lukewarmers are people who have a hard time believing that lukewarming causes beheadings.

9. Paris, December 1, 2015

What I am hearing is that the heads of state are planning to clap each other on the back and say this is a very successful conference.

—James E. Hansen,
Paris, December 2015

At 8:40 a.m. EST on December 1, 2015, the White House live-streamed President Obama's press conference from the Paris summit. He reiterated that the United States would sign no treaty that contained legally binding language regarding cuts in carbon dioxide emissions. For example, if the final document said that the signatories "shall" reduce emissions by a particular amount, the United States would not sign because that would make the agreement a treaty that could not be approved by the required two-thirds of the U.S. Senate. As a consequence, it would lack the force of U.S. law. The political calculus would remain the same no matter which party controls the Senate. The demographics of the states—with a semi-permanent bloc of red-state Republican seats comprising far more than a third of the Senate—assure that this will be the case for the foreseeable future.

Obama did say, however, that the United States would allow certain other aspects of the agreement to become binding, but only those unlikely (he assumed) to provoke a successful judicial challenge concerning the agreement's validity as a treaty. The specific language he said the United States could approve concerned each signatory's ability to revise its Intended Nationally Determined Contribution (INDC) to greenhouse gas emissions reductions. The logic goes something like this: because the INDCs are voluntary, the Paris agreement only "binds" the United States to voluntarily revise its commitment (intention).

When questioned about enforcement of voluntary INDCs, Secretary of State John Kerry said that nations that fail to live up to their intended commitments would be punished with "shame," which he deemed "the most powerful weapon" capable of enforcing the Paris agreement.

Responding to the president's press conference, Senate Majority Leader Mitch McConnell (R-KY) noted Obama, without congressional approval, had been going it alone on climate change for years and that the president was trying to sell his independent action as an American "commitment" to the Paris agreement. Sen. McConnell said on December 1, 2015:

> The president simply went around Congress to impose similarly regressive—and likely illegal—'power plan' energy regulations anyway. He's currently trying to sell that power plan to world leaders in Paris as proof of the American government's commitment to his energy priorities.[1]

So far no one has succeeded in triggering judicial modification of *Massachusetts v. Environmental Protection Agency*. Until someone is able to do that, any president can continue in the same manner as Obama and take executive action. As a consequence, it's fair to conclude any executive action concerning a "commitment" to the Paris agreement depends on who is in the White House. It's difficult to conclude that a potential President Trump who, in a 2014 tweet referred to global warming as a hoax, will enforce whatever commitment comes out of the Paris conference. Similarly, the Republicans' other near-front runner, Senator Ted Cruz (R-TX), submitted a bill in 2015 that would have forbidden federal executive agencies from regulating carbon dioxide under the Clean Air Act, as amended. Were a bill similar to the one Cruz offered become law, the effect would be legislative nullification of the Supreme Court's 2007 ruling.

---

[1] On February 9, 2016, the Supreme Court voted 5-4 to "stay" EPA's "Clean Power Plan" pending judicial review.

10. California Cascade

> A massive campaign must be launched to restore a high-quality environment in North America and to de-develop the United States. . . . De-development means bringing our economic system (especially patterns of consumption) into line with the realities of ecology and the global resource situation. . . . Redistribution of wealth both within and among nations is absolutely essential, if a decent life is to be provided for every human being.
>
> —John Holdren*

The Middle East isn't the only place in the world with a Mediterranean climate. Such climates are found in some of the nicest places on earth—southwestern Australia and California, for example. Each has problems with occasional droughts of gargantuan proportion. This is because they also are very sunny climates that, in the absence of rain, get bone-dry very quickly. Nonetheless, California's governor Jerry Brown seems to have no problem goosing the availability cascade in blaming California's drought on global warming (what he calls "climate change").[1, 2]

---

* John Holdren is a senior adviser to President Barack Obama on science and technology issues. He serves as assistant to the president for science and technology, director of the White House Office on Science and Technology Policy, and co-chair of the President's Council of Advisers on Science and Technology.

[1] For Wikipedia, this isn't a bad definition:

> The Mediterranean climate is characterized by warm to hot, dry summers and mild to cool, wet winters. Mediterranean climate zones are associated with the five large subtropical high-pressure cells of the oceans: the Azores High, South Atlantic High, North Pacific High, South Pacific High, and Indian Ocean High. These climatological high-pressure cells shift towards the poles in the summer and towards the equator in the winter, playing a major role in the formation of the world's subtropical and tropical deserts as well as the Mediterranean Basin's climate.

[2] "'I can tell you, from California, climate change is not a hoax,' [Governor Brown] told ABC's *This Week*. 'We're dealing with it, and it's damn serious.'" Joseph Neese, "Jerry Brown on California Drought: 'Climate Change Is Not a Hoax,'" MSNBC, April 5, 2015, http://www.msnbc.com/msnbc/jerry-brown-california-drought-climate-change-not-hoax.

As the drought entered its third year with spring snowpack in the Sierra Nevada mountains at record low levels, conditions prompted Governor Brown to enact statewide water restrictions. He and the press have seemed eager to blame our greenhouse gas-spewing modern economy as the drought's primary culprit. The problem is, most scientific research suggests the absence of precipitation in California has its roots in natural variability. Interestingly, a recent paper by Thomas Delworth and several colleagues finds a common cause for both the western U.S. drought and the apparent pause in global warming.[3, 4]

Early in 2015, a study by Jim Johnstone and Nathan Mantua found that naturally-occurring atmospheric pressure patterns across the northeast Pacific Ocean—patterns they traced back more than 100 years—could explain virtually all of the increase in temperature over large portions of the Pacific Northwest, extending into northern California. As for southern California, the same patterns explain a bit more than half the long-term, observed temperature increase. They write, "These results suggest that natural internally generated changes in atmospheric circulation were the primary cause of coastal NE Pacific warming from 1900 to 2012 and demonstrate more generally that regional mechanisms of inter-annual and multi-decadal temperature variability can also extend to century time scales."[5]

Prominent climate bloggers—Andrew Freedman at *Mashable*, among them—paid no attention to this important work in writing about California's situation. "We are now seeing the rise of a new, supercharged type of drought, in which global warming-related temperature extremes combine with dry conditions to transform what would otherwise be an ordinary drought event into a far more severe event," Freedman writes.[6]

[3] Thomas Delworth et al., "A Link between the Hiatus in Global Warming and North American Drought," *Journal of Climate* 28 (2015): 3834–45.

[4] Of course it would be pretty cheeky to blame the recent pause in global warming (as seen in the Remote Sensing System's monthly satellite data) on global warming. But linking it to the California drought is downright elegant.

[5] James A. Johnstone and Nathan J. Mantua, "Atmospheric Controls on Northeast Pacific Temperature Variability and Change, 1900–2012," *Proceedings of the National Academy of Sciences* 111 (2014): 14360–65.

[6] Andrew Freedman, "Epic California Drought Is Preview of Future Global Warming Mega-Droughts," *Mashable* (blog), April 2, 2015, http://mashable.com /2015/04/02/california-drought-preview-global-warming-megadrought.

If only things were so simple. But they're not. Several factors confound such a hasty conclusion.

Drought begets high temperatures and vice versa. When conditions are dry, incoming solar radiation isn't diverted into evaporating moisture from the surface (called "latent heating" because you don't feel it). Instead, the additional radiation goes toward further raising the surface temperature (called "sensible heating" because you can feel it). So, the absence of precipitation (itself linked to natural variability) helps lead to higher temperatures, which lead to worsening drought conditions. No global warming is necessary for this to happen.

Further, many of the same elements of natural variability that have been linked to the precipitation deficit also act to elevate temperature, as shown by Johnstone and Mantua. But their analysis ends in 2012. What about the time since then—the years encompassing California's drought and record high temperatures?

We wrote to Dr. Johnstone and asked whether there were any updates to their analysis. He wrote back, directing us to a page on his website used to update the study. There we found that the naturally occurring atmospheric pressure pattern that the two researchers linked to the long-term warming across California (and the Pacific Northwest) has been very high during the past several years. In fact, it reached its highest anomalies on record during early 2015. In other words, the same mechanism that explains the majority of the observed temperature rise in California since the beginning of the 20th century also explains why it has been especially hot in California of late. Again, global warming need not be a factor.[7]

Dr. Johnstone went on to say, "The model under-predicts the magnitude of the current warm anomaly, but this is typical of strong peaks." This sort of behavior—underprediction of extreme values—is commonplace in the statistical methodology (linear regression analysis) that Johnstone and Mantua employed. The impact of global warming may be residing within this underprediction, although it likely would be sharing that space with drought-induced high temperatures, local landscape changes (e.g., urban warming), a nonlinear response to atmospheric pressure forcing,

[7] James A. Johnstone, "NE Pacific Coastal Warming Due to Changes in Atmospheric Circulation," http://www.jajstone.com.

and a host of other circulation factors. In other words, any impact of human-caused global warming on recent high temperatures in California (and their influence on drought conditions) is minor at best and not deserving of the level of credit that good folks like Freedman and Governor Brown bestow upon it.

While this conclusion is supported by the scientific literature and basic climatology, it is absent in popular press coverage of the ongoing drought. As the late Paul Harvey would say, "And that's the rest of the story." And as a lukewarmer might say, "That's the availability cascade."

11. Outside the Cascade: Reality Bites

> It doesn't matter what is true; it only matters what people believe is true.

> —Paul Watson*

First, a bit of physics. There is a logarithmic response of lower atmospheric temperature to changes in the concentration of carbon dioxide. As a result, early incremental increases in a greenhouse gas concentration create the largest warming. As the concentration increases, the warming begins to damp-off so that equal changes in the concentration result in less and less warming.

It has been known for a long time—not as a result of dubious climate modeling—that the direct warming for a doubling in the atmospheric concentration of carbon dioxide should be around 1.0°C (1.8°F), which is far below the modeled average of 3.2°C (5.8°F) that appears in the most recent climate compendium published by the UN's Intergovernmental Panel on Climate Change in 2013.

The higher prediction is due to climate models amplifying warming by a factor of three. They accomplish this by assuming that the increments of warming caused by carbon dioxide increase evaporation of water from Earth's vast oceans, thereby increasing the amount of water vapor—another greenhouse gas. This causes the temperature to rise some more, which causes more evaporation, and so on.

The climate models don't take Earth's surface temperature to a runaway greenhouse effect, which could stop only when the temperature reached somewhere around 1,100°C (2,000°F). Despite the models' failure to make that projection, former NASA scientist James Hansen has written that a runaway greenhouse effect is a virtual

---

* Paul Watson is a Canadian environmental activist and founder of the Sea Shepherd Society. He often is credited with founding Greenpeace, although the organization denies it and instead characterizes him as "an influential early member" despite his service on the Greenpeace board and his claim to have attended the meeting that led to the group's creation.

certainty were all of Earth's fossil fuel reserves (petroleum, natural gas, coal, tar sands, and tar shales) to be consumed.[1]

Could he possibly be correct? After all, the forecast of various environmental apocalypses are by now a dime a dozen. As it turns out, our planet ran this experiment 56 million years ago. A prolonged series of massive volcanic eruptions spewed about three billion tons of carbon dioxide per year into the atmosphere for 20,000 years. That's a total load of about 60,000 billion metric tons. The event is known as the Paleocene–Eocene Thermal Maximum. Tropical ocean temperatures rose about 5°C (9°F). There was no runaway greenhouse effect.[2, 3]

If all current proven fossil fuel reserves were burned, they would dump about 4,000 billion metric tons of carbon dioxide into the atmosphere. While that doesn't seem like much, compared with what went into the air during the Paleocene–Eocene Thermal Maximum, the concentration of atmospheric CO_2 is rising at a much faster rate than it did back then. Could the faster rise in the concentration of CO_2 cause a runaway greenhouse effect?

According to Colin Goldblatt of the University of Victoria, Canada, and Andrew Watson then at the University of East Anglia, UK, that's unlikely to happen:

> The good news is that almost all lines of evidence lead us to believe that it is unlikely to be possible, even in principle, to trigger a full runaway greenhouse by addition of non-condensible greenhouse gases such as carbon dioxide to the atmosphere. . . . We cannot . . . completely rule out the possibility that human actions might cause a transition, if not to full runaway, then at least to a much warmer climate state than the present one. *High climate sensitivity might provide a warning*.[4] [emphasis added]

[1]James Hansen, *Storms of My Grandchildren: The Truth about the Coming Climate Catastrophe and Our Last Chance to Save Humanity* (New York: Bloomsbury, 2009), p. 304.

[2]James C. Zachos et al., "A Transient Rise in Tropical Sea Surface Temperature during the Paleocene–Eocene Thermal Maximum," *Science* 302 (2003): 1551–54.

[3]In the authors' lifetimes, we so far have survived predictions of a silent spring, the population bomb, global famine, oxygen depletion, global cooling, forest die-off from acid rain, and global warming. We expect similarly to survive predictions of the next one: ocean acidification.

[4]Colin Goldblatt and Andrew J. Watson, "The Runaway Greenhouse: Implications for Future Climate Change, Geoengineering, and Planetary Atmospheres," *Philosophical Transactions of The Royal Society A* 370 (2012): 4197–216.

If high climate sensitivity might provide a warning, then it follows that low climate sensitivity should provide reassurance. After Goldblatt and Watson published their paper in 2012, Hansen walked back his forecast, citing (in part) the Paleocene–Eocene Thermal Maximum.[5]

Lukewarmers note that the Earth already has run an experiment in which atmospheric carbon dioxide increased much more than it will be able to do from human activity, and there was no runaway greenhouse effect.

[5]James E. Hansen, "Making Things Clearer: Exaggeration, Jumping the Gun, and the Venus Syndrome," *Columbia University*, April 15, 2013, http://www.columbia.edu/~jeh1/mailings/2013/20130415_Exaggerations.pdf.

12. Breaking Up with Your Forecast Is Hard to Do

> No matter if the science is all phony, there are collateral environmental benefits. . . . Climate change [provides] the greatest chance to bring about justice and equality in the world.

—Christine Stewart*

Late in 1997, a massive temperature wave of unknown origin propagated eastward across the western Pacific to the coast of Peru. It was so strong that it reversed the northeasterly trade winds that dominate the lower latitudes north of the thermal equator. A persistent reversal of the trade winds often begins in December and is called El Niño (the male child) because of its proximity to Christmas. When it is very large or very persistent, it exerts a profound influence on much of Earth's climate. It also can fool climatologists.

During an El Niño, global average surface temperature spikes, in part because the reversal of the trade winds suppresses the upwelling of a large amount of subsurface cold water off the coast of South America. The 1998 peak in global surface temperature was (at that time) the record high in a 137-year modern history. It was so big that Thomas Karl, who directs the U.S. National Climatic Data Center, declared it to be a "change point"—by which he meant global warming would from then on accelerate beyond its so-far embarrassingly torpid pace.[1]

Nature doesn't listen to scientists. Just as the warming of the Remote Sensing Systems (RSS) satellite record dead-stopped as soon as the greens touted it as the antidote to Spencer and Christy's no-warming history, so it appears the earth stopped warming as soon as Karl pronounced the change point.[2]

---

*A member of the Liberal Party, Christine Stewart was Canada's minister of the environment from 1997–99 until she resigned before the 2000 elections.

[1] The National Climatic Data Center's new name (National Centers for Environmental Information-Climate) doesn't seem to be catching on.

[2] Unless you believe that he was able to "disappear" the pause some 18 years later by getting rid of some inconvenient data (see the next chapter).

Figure 11

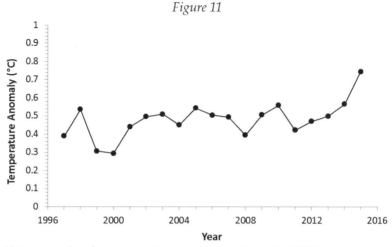

Note: Annual surface average temperature beginning in 1997.[3]

According to Cato Institute scholar Ross McKitrick, using the newest surface record from the Climate Research Unit at the University of East Anglia in the United Kingdom, we were in the 19th year of the pause when he published in 2014 (Figure 11). As of March 2016, the revised lower atmospheric monthly satellite records from the University of Alabama–Huntsville show a pause that is 19.5 years in length even with the record warmth caused by El Niño in early 2016 (Figure 12). The mid-tropospheric RSS record recently has been revised, but the lower tropospheric data (which is most appropriate in discussing surface temperatures) were not.[4, 5, 6, 7]

[3] Colin P. Morice et al., "Quantifying Uncertainties in Global and Regional Temperature Change Using an Ensemble of Observational Estimates: The HadCRUT4 Data Set," *Journal of Geophysical Research* 117 (2012): D08101.

[4] The HadCRUT4 dataset replaced its predecessor, HadCRUT3, in 2012.

[5] These are the two most highly cited analyses of the Microwave Sounding Unit data that began accumulating late in 1978.

[6] R. McKitrick, "HAC-Robust Measurement of the Duration of a Trendless Subsample in a Global Climate Time Series," *Open Journal of Statistics* 4 (2014): 527–35.

[7] See Footnote 1 in Chapter 1 with regard to a recent revision of the RSS record.

Figure 12

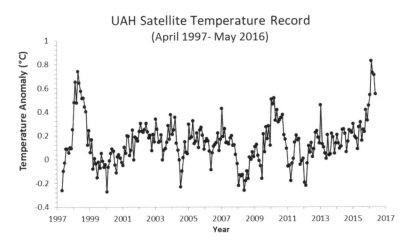

Note: According to the latest version of the University of Alabama–Huntsville (UAH) record as recently revised to account for changing on-board sensors and orbital mechanics. Even with the El Niño peak at the end of the record, there's no statistically significant warming for over 19 years.[8]

No one has yet acknowledged the absence of corroboration for the change point pronouncement by the head of the National Climatic Data Center, just as no climate modeler has admitted that his or her models run too hot.

❝

---

[8] Data from Roy W. Spencer, John R. Christy, and William D. Braswell, "UAH Version 6 Global Satellite Temperature Products: Methodology and Results," http://www.drroyspencer.com/2015/04/version-6-0-of-the-uah-temperature-dataset-released-new-lt-trend-0-11-cdecade. (Submitted to *Asia Pacific Journal of Atmospheric Sciences* in 2016.)

13. Is the Pause Just an Artifact of Bad Data?

> So, yes, climate scientists might exaggerate, but in today's world this is the only way to assure any political action and thus more federal funding.

> —Monika Kopacz*

After a substantial publicity buildup, *Science Express* (the online preprint of *Science* magazine) on June 4, 2015, published a paper by Tom Karl and several colleagues claiming that the pause in global warming, which they dubbed a hiatus, simply was an artifact of bad data—especially temperature readings taken at the sea's surface (sea-surface temperatures or SSTs).[1]

Their conclusion was based on a newly released revision of the Extended Reconstructed Sea-Surface Temperature, version 4 (ERSSTv4). Sea-surface temperatures always have been difficult to measure directly. Satellite records of SSTs in recent decades are the most reliable. Inexplicably, version 4 "disincluded" (Karl's word) the satellite data because of a slight cold bias detected when recording began in the 1980s (a bias that is easily accounted for).[2]

ERSSTv4 relies on three main sources for its data: water temperature measured at the cooling water intake ports of marine vessels (a dataset that begins around the end of World War II), a growing network of drifting buoys, and—prior to the war—temperature measurements collected from canvas buckets thrown overboard then hauled back onboard to record the temperature of the water in the bucket.

---

* Monika Kopacz is a program officer within the National Oceanic and Atmospheric Administration's climate program office.

[1] Thomas R. Karl et al., "Possible Artifacts of Data Biases in the Recent Global Surface Warming Hiatus," *Science* 26 (2015): 1469–72.

[2] Boyin Huang et al., "Extended Reconstructed Sea-Surface Temperature Version 4 (ERSST.v4). Part 1: Upgrades and Intercomparisons," *Journal of Climate* 28 (2015): 911–30.

The shipboard data are horrific. Ships conduct a massive amount of heat, both from the sun and the ship's engines. There's a voluminous literature on the inaccuracy of intake-tube temperatures. The measurement errors are estimated to be an order of magnitude larger than any multidecadal signal in the data. The tubes are at different depths in the water depending on the ship's size and configuration, so data from them hardly represent sea-surface temperature. The canvas bucket data suffer from a different problem: water in the buckets evaporates in the wind as the buckets are hauled upward and back onboard. The evaporation results in a spurious cooling. That leaves the expanding buoy network as a possibly reliable source.

The buoys are designed to measure temperature using calibrated instruments at a standard height above the water. Inexplicably, the new record—aside from the disincluded satellite data—adjusts each reading on every buoy upward 0.12°C (0.22°F). This is done, Karl explains, to make the buoy data "homogeneous" with the crappy intake-tube data. Adjusting good data upward so that they will better match bad data seems a questionable technique, to say the least.

What Karl and his colleagues have done is to force a warming trend into the pause (hiatus). This happens because there's increasingly more buoy data displacing ship data. The increasing density of the adjusted data consequently will result in a warmer average, everything else being equal.

The difference between the versions of sea-surface temperatures that include satellite data and those that don't occurs at a fortuitous time.

As shown in Figure 13, ERSSTv4 introduces a cooling trend into the last two decades of data in the third version prior to the pause. The record becomes successively warmer after the pause begins.

The authors' main claim—that they have uncovered a significant recent warming trend—is dubious. The significance level they report in their findings (0.10) hardly is normative and its use should prompt members of the scientific community to question the reasoning behind the use of such a lax standard.[3, 4]

---

[3] "It is also noteworthy that the new global trends are statistically significant and positive at the 0.10 significance level for 1998-2012." Karl et al., "Possible Artifacts."

[4] The comments tendered to *Science* are the most negative and scathing we ever have seen concerning a climate paper published in a high-impact journal. See http://www.americanthinker.com/blog/2015/07/commenters_excoriate_a_emscienceem_paper_that_denies_global_warming_pause.html.

Figure 13

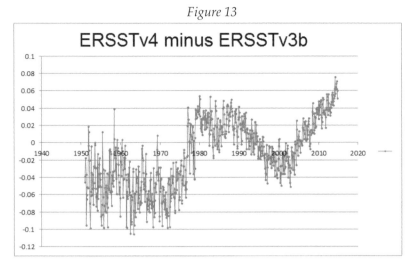

ERSSTv4 minus ERSSTv3b

Note: Differences between the 2015 version of the SST and its predecessor. The 2015 version "disincludes" the more accurate satellite readings and treats the buoy data in such a way as to guarantee a warming trend during the period of the pause.[5]

The authors also mention extending high-latitude land data over the Arctic Ocean, as is done in some versions of NASA's global temperature history. While they did not do this in their paper, they allude to the idea that they should have done so and note that adding it would have induced even more warming. This extension is highly questionable. Much of the Arctic Ocean is ice covered—even in high summer—meaning that the surface temperature *must* remain near freezing. Extending land data into the ocean obviously will induce substantially exaggerated temperatures.

Additionally, there are other measures of bulk lower atmosphere temperatures—like those from satellites or weather balloons—that are independent of surface measurements and clearly show the pause.[6]

Soon after Karl's paper was published, NASA incorporated the ERSSTv4 data, also forcing a warming trend into the data since 1998.

[5] From the website *KNMI Climate Explorer,* http://climexp.knmi.nl/start.cgi?id =someone@somewhere. Analysis by authors.

[6] See, for example, Figure 1 in Chapter 2.

The regularly updated global history from the Climate Research Unit at the University of East Anglia long has used a sea-surface temperature record generated by the United Kingdom Meteorological Office. They recently extended new land records out into the Arctic Ocean, which is hardly defensible over a mixed water-ice ocean where the surface temperature must remain near freezing. This has induced an increasingly warm bias into the record, but insufficient to dispel the "pause" from 1997 through 2014.[7]

Georgia Tech's Judith Curry has this to say about the switch in data:

> In my opinion, the gold standard dataset for global ocean surface temperatures is the UK dataset, HadSST3. A review of the uncertainties is given in this paper by John Kennedy http://www.metoffice.gov.uk/hadobs/hadsst3/uncertainty.html. Note, the UK group has dealt with the same issues raised by the NOAA team. I personally see no reason to use the NOAA ERSST dataset, I do not see any evidence that the NOAA group has done anywhere near as careful a job as the UK group in processing the ocean temperatures.[8]

Finally, assuming for a moment that all of the adjustments the authors applied ultimately prove themselves to be justified and accurate, the temperature trend they report from 1998–2014 remains significantly below the mean trend projected by the collection of climate models used in the most recent report from the UN Intergovernmental Panel on Climate Change.

Lukewarmers recognize that the central issue of human-caused climate change is not a question of whether or not it is warming, but rather a question of how much. The response to this relevant question has been (and remains) that the warming is taking place at a much slower rate than is being projected, with the pause or without it.

Given the behavior represented in Figure 14, maybe it's time to conduct an overall test of all the climate models.

---

[7] The El Niño-related peak in 2015 limits the pause in the East Anglia record to 18 years. Such events are often followed by an equal and opposite drop in temperatures, so the pause may reappear later in this decade.

[8] Judith Curry, "Has NOAA Busted the Pause in Global Warming?" *Climate Etc.* (blog), June 4, 2015, http://judithcurry.com/2015/06/04/has-noaa-busted-the-pause-in-global-warming.

Figure 14

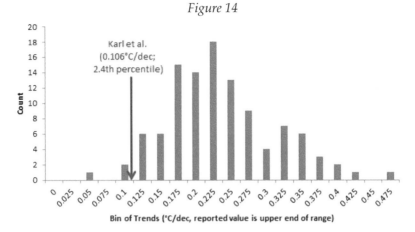

Bin of Trends (°C/dec, reported value is upper end of range)

Note: Distribution of trends in projected global average surface temperature from 1998–2014 as represented by the 108 climate model runs used in the latest report of the UN Intergovernmental Panel on Climate Change (IPCC). The models were run with historical climate forcings through 2005 and extended to 2014 using the IPCC's low–midrange emissions scenario (technically, RCP4.5). The surface temperature trend over the same period, as reported by Karl and his colleagues in 2015 is included in red. Their surface temperature trend falls at the 2.4th percentile of the model distribution and indicates a value that is significantly below the models' mean projection.[9]

[9] Climate model data from the website *KNMI Climate Explorer*, http://climexp .knmi.nl/start.cgi?id=someone@somewhere; observed data from Karl et al., "Possible Artifacts"; and analysis by authors.

14. Testing the Climate Models

> First, we guess it, no, don't laugh, that's really true. Then we compute the consequences of the guess, to see what, if this is right, if this law we guess is right, to see what it would imply and then we compare the computation results to nature, or we say compare to experiment or experience, compare it directly with observations to see if it works. If it disagrees with experiment, it's wrong. In that simple statement is the key to science. It doesn't make any difference how beautiful your guess is, it doesn't matter how smart you are, who made the guess, or what his name is. . . .If it disagrees with experiment, it's wrong. That's all there is to it.
>
> —Richard Feynman*

In its most basic form, science consists of statements of hypotheses that are retained by critical tests against observations. Climate models also are generating hypotheses—be they forecasts for the future (which obviously cannot be tested), hindcasts for the past, or statements about how our climate should have evolved as atmospheric concentrations of greenhouse gases and other industrial emissions have increased. Clearly, if the models cannot properly simulate the past, they can't be relied upon for the future. If they could do so, then they might provide some reasonable guidance.

What primarily drives climate changes in a greenhouse gas-enhanced atmosphere is a change in the distribution of heat within the atmosphere. This is largely expressed as a warming of Earth's surface and a cooling of the stratosphere. Concern about surface warming is obvious. So, how well have the climate models simulated this important variable?

Over the past 30 years (1986–2015), the suite of 108 climate model runs used in the 2013 compendium assembled by the UN Intergovernmental Panel on Climate Change produces an average surface warming rate of 2.6°C (4.7°F) per century. The observed value since

---

*Nobel Laureate in Physics, 1965.

the mid-1970s (and including the "pause") is about 1.6°C (2.9°F), or about 40 percent less than what the models forecast should have happened over the past 30 years. Does this signal that the models are failing?

In order to answer that question, one must conduct a systematic analysis of climate model behavior. We analyzed the data since 1950 for the 108 model runs used in the 2013 IPCC scientific assessment available from the KNMI Climate Explorer (http://climexp.KNMI. nl). We examined the predicted trends for periods beginning in the past 10 years (2005–14), then 11 (2004–14), and so on all the way back to 1951–2014. The shortest period appears as the rightmost data point in Figure 15.

We calculated the average warming produced by the 108 models at the following percentile values: 2.5, 5.0, 95.0, and 97.5 percent. The 5th and 95th percentiles are represented by the light gray lines in Figure 15, while the broken lines depict the 2.5 and 97.5 percentiles. The average predicted trend is represented by the dark gray line near the midpoint of the percentile bounds.

We compared these trends with the trends observed in the Had-CRU4 (University of East Anglia Climate Research Unit) temperature history. They show up as circles. When the circles are open, the observed trends are within the 95th percentile confidence limits of the model ensemble. Where the circles are gray, the observed trends are below the 5th percentile, and where they are black, they are below the 2.5 percentile.[1]

In summary, we found: (1) every observed trend, from 1951–2014 to 2005–14 falls below the model average; (2) the observed trend initially fell below the 5th percentile in 1977 and remained there through 2012; (3) the observed trend initially fell below the 2.5 percentile trend in 1980; and (4) since 1980, there are only four trends between the 2.5 and 5th percentiles. If the modeled trends were systematically lower, their predictions would pass the test of the hypothesis they represent. But they don't. The models' sensitivity is too high.

---

[1] Patrick J. Michaels and Paul C. Knappenberger, "Quantifying the Lack of Consistency between Climate Model Projections and Observations of the Evolution of the Earth's Average Surface Temperature since the Mid-20th Century," a presentation to the 2014 fall meeting of the American Geophysical Union, San Francisco, CA, December 16–19.

Figure 15

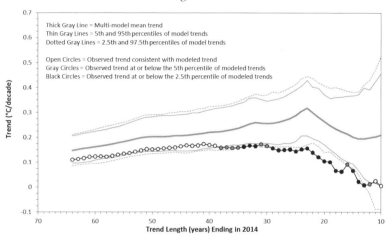

Note: The results indicate that the ensemble behavior of the 108 model runs fail to pass a normative test of hypothesis. See text for description.

Lukewarmers believe that hypotheses—including climate forecasts—should be tested according to the normative rules of science.

15. Paris, December 4, 2015

> In this regard, for a lasting solution to the climate crisis we
> must destroy Capitalism.
>
> —Boliva's Intended Nationally
> Determined Contribution, Paris

Nations that fuel free markets with fossil energy can become rich very fast. Consider horse-drawn London in the early 19th century compared with conditions some 50 years later when people were able to move about in relative comfort using a subterranean railroad. The London Underground's first line opened in 1863.

The common progression whereby underdeveloped nations begin developing and then become developed caused quite a row in Paris as the first week of COP-21 drew to a close.

China's economy is undergoing an explosion of expansion in urban infrastructure. The nation bears little resemblance to what it was during the reign of Mao Tse-Tung. Even so, China still is considered to be a developing nation.

The Intended Nationally Determined Contribution (INDC) process ensured there would be little to fight about in Paris concerning the voluntary emissions reductions to which each nation agreed, whether its INDC was inconsequential regarding further development (e.g., India and China) or economically consequential and likely impossible (e.g., the United States). What was left to haggle about concerned money, specifically who was to pay and how much.

India became particularly upset because wealthy countries like the United States recognize the rapid changes occurring in the developing world. As the world becomes much wealthier in the 21st century (a strong and robust prediction from virtually every developmental economist, including those of the UN), then there will be a greater number of nations able to pay the remaining poorer nations and enabling them to purchase technologies that never really will power very much of their economies.

Todd Stern, the U.S. special envoy to Paris noted, "There are developing countries moving to being donors. [The United States] recognizes that there are more advanced developing countries." Hearing that, India and others expressed concern that such thinking could eventually force them to become contributors to the campaigns for use of solar energy and windmills.

India's Susheel Kumar was especially upset, feeling this ran counter to the spirit of the 1992 Framework Convention on Climate Change that had spoken of "common but differentiated responsibilities" whereby rich nations would contribute money to poor countries so that they could use "sustainable" technologies to develop themselves.

Stern tried to soothe India's concerns in responding that, under the Paris agreement, no developing country would be obliged to do this. Why? Because, pursuant to the Paris agreement, *everything* is voluntary (except that signatory nations agree to revise their INDCs every five years). Every INDC toward emissions reductions is precisely as its name implies: intended. And so is every commitment to provide money sometime in the future. Stern said, "Some people have overreacted or read it incorrectly." Mr. Kumar, perhaps?

At the same time, another kerfuffle broke out concerning who would verify if a nation would meet its intended contribution. As things stand, the rules for developing countries to report emissions are very lax. They aren't above creating political gain by enabling developing nations not to tell the truth or find it.

In the past, such practices have cost the UN process its credibility. For example, when Robert T. Watson, an American, headed the Intergovernmental Panel on Climate Change (IPCC), he used his position to harangue the United States. During a 2001 IPCC meeting in Shanghai, he said:

> The United States is way off meeting its [emissions] targets [agreed to under the Kyoto Protocol]. A country like China has done more, in my opinion, than a country like the United States to move forward in economic development while remaining environmentally sensitive.

Watson's judgment might have been clouded by Shanghai's miasmatic air when he chose to accept Chinese government claims that their nation's carbon dioxide emissions decreased from 1996–2000 despite electricity generation increasing exponentially. It's an obvious impossibility. Such a glaring inconsistency and satellite-sensed measurements of the quantity of coal consumed in China compelled the Chinese to substantially revise their emissions figures. For example, in 2007, they increased their 2000 emissions figure by 23 percent.[1]

A similar thing happened again in 2015. It turns out the post-2000 data was just as bad as the unadjusted late-1990s data that Watson uncritically had accepted as evidence of China's ability to control its carbon dioxide emissions.

Three weeks before the start of the Paris Summit, the *New York Times* reported, "China . . . has been burning up to 17 percent more coal a year than the government previously disclosed [and] coal consumption has been underestimated since 2000." In other words, China has vastly understated its emissions *for the last two decades*!

President Obama realized that if developing nations (including China) continue to underreport emissions, the credibility of the Paris agreement could evaporate. In his speech opening the Paris conference, he said, "Here in Paris, let's agree to a strong system of transparency that gives each of us confidence that all of us are meeting our commitment." Dr. Ajay Mathur, director of India's Bureau of Energy Efficiency responded there was "no need to spend time again negotiating new reporting guidelines and rules." This despite China's obviously politically-motivated fiddling with its data from 1996–2015.

$$\text{\textbf{999}}$$

---

[1] Gregg H. Marland, Thomas A. Boden, and Robert J. Andres, "Global, Regional, and National Fossil Fuel CO_2 Emissions," in *Trends: A Compendium of Data on Global Change* (Oak Ridge, TN: Carbon Dioxide Information and Analysis Center, 2008), http://cdiac.ornl.gov/trends/emis/overview.html.

16. If You Explain Everything, You Explain Nothing

Statements or systems of statements, in order to be ranked as scientific, must be capable of conflicting with possible, or conceivable, observations.

—Karl Popper[*]

In illustration of grand narratives and availability cascades, consider the following:

Hurricanes are worse because of global warming.[1]

Hurricanes are fewer in number because of global warming.[2]

Winter storms are stronger because of global warming.[3]

Winter storms are weaker because of global warming.[4]

Crop yields are going down because of global warming.[5]

---

[*] Karl Popper, *Conjectures and Refutations: The Growth of Scientific Knowledge* (London: Rutledge and Kegan Paul, 1963). Popper (1902–94) was an Austrian-British philosopher considered to be one of the greatest science philosophers of the 20th century.

[1] Kerry Emanuel, "Increasing Destructiveness of Tropical Cyclones over the Past 30 years," *Nature* 436 (2005): 686–88.

[2] Lennart Bengtsson, Michael Botzet, and Monika Esch, "Will Greenhouse Gas-Induced Warming over the Next 50 Years Lead to Higher Frequency and Greater Intensity of Hurricanes?" *Tellus A* 48 (1996): 57–73.

[3] Travis Madsen and Nathan Willcox, "When It Rains, It Pours: Global Warming and the Increase in Extreme Precipitation from 1948 to 2011" (Boston: Environment Research and Policy Center, 2012) available from the website *Environment America*, http://www.environmentamerica.org/reports/ame/when-it-rains-it-pours.

[4] Brian J. Hoskins and Kevin I. Hodges, "New Perspectives on the Northern Hemisphere Winter Storm Tracks," *Journal of the Atmospheric Sciences* 59 (2002): 1041–61.

[5] Wolfram Schlenker and Michael J. Roberts, "Nonlinear Temperature Effects Indicate Severe Damages to U.S. Crop Yields under Climate Change," *Proceedings of the National Academy of Sciences* 106 (2009): 15594–98.

Crop yields are going up because of global warming.[6, 7]
Global warming makes mid-latitude winters warmer.[8]
Global warming makes mid-latitude winters colder.[9]
Global warming increases mortality in urban heat waves.[10]
Global warming decreases mortality in urban heat waves.[11]

It seems as though global warming explains everything. Whatever the weather anomaly du jour, Matt Drudge will be able to link to a study relating it to global warming. Of course, most of the reasoning is post hoc. Examples abound.

In 2000, David Viner of the British Meteorological Office told the London *Independent* that, in a very few years, snowstorms would become "a rare and exciting event." That was after a few winters with very little snow in southern England. Michael Oppenheimer (at the time Barbra Streisand Chair of Environmental Studies at the Environmental Defense Fund) waxed nostalgic for the lost snows of his youth. He told the *New York Times* in January 2000 that he lamented his daughter hadn't used her sled in over four years. Global warming was to blame.[12, 13]

[6] Rattan Lal, "Soil Carbon Sequestration Impacts on Global Climate Change and Food Security," *Science* 304 (2004): 1623–27.

[7] Keith W. Jaggard, Aiming Qi, and Eric S. Ober, "Possible Changes to Arable Crop Yields by 2050," *Philosophical Transactions of the Royal Society B* 365 (2010): 2835–51.

[8] James A. Screen, "Arctic Amplification Decreases Temperature Variance in Northern Mid- to High-Latitudes," *Nature Climate Change* 4 (2014): 577–82.

[9] Quihong Tang et al., "Cold Winter Extremes in Northern Continents Linked to Arctic Sea Ice Loss," *Environmental Research Letters* 8 (2013).

[10] Elisaveta P. Petkova et al., "Projected Heat-Related Mortality in the U.S. Urban Northeast," *International Journal of Environmental Research and Public Health* 10 (2013): 6734–47.

[11] Robert E. Davis et al., "Changing Heat-Related Mortality in the United States," *Environmental Health Perspectives* 111 (2003): 1712–18, http://www.ncbi.nlm.nih.gov/pmc/articles/PMC1241712/pdf/ehp0111-001712.pdf.

[12] Charles Onians, "Snowfalls Are Now Just a Thing of the Past," *Independent* [UK], March 20, 2000, http://www.independent.co.uk/environment/snowfalls-are-now-just-a-thing-of-the-past-724017.html.

[13] Barbara Stewart, "Winter in New York: Something's Missing; Absence of Snow Upsets Rhythms of Urban Life and Natural World," *New York Times*, January 15, 2000, http://www.nytimes.com/2000/01/15/nyregion/winter-new-york-something-s-missing-absence-snow-upsets-rhythms-urban-life.html.

Figure 16

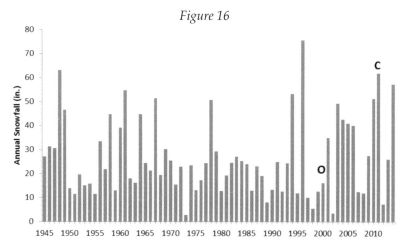

Note: Postwar snow in Central Park. The "O" denotes when Michael Oppenheimer in the *New York Times* decried the lack of snow due to global warming since 1996. "C" is when Judah Cohen told the *Times* that the heavy snows of recent years had been caused by global warming.

Within three years, snow returned to both New York (Figure 16) and the United Kingdom. In the winter of 2009–10, Washington, D.C., was hit by three official blizzards. At the latitude and altitude of the District of Columbia (where summers can be as bad as in Lima, Peru, during an El Niño) a single blizzard is an extreme rarity. Soon after, long-range forecaster Judah Cohen gave us an explanation (again as reported by the *Times*)—they were caused by global warming.[14]

Hindsight may be golden, but in science post hoc reasoning is poison. As Karl Popper notes in his most famous essay, science that explains everything isn't science because it can't be tested. He calls it pseudoscience. Two of his favorite examples are Freudian psychiatry and communism.[15]

Popper views science to be at its best when it makes difficult predictions. Einstein made one: gravity bends light. Sure enough, when Arthur Eddington studied the total eclipse of 1919, he noted that the light from stars appearing near the sun's darkened limb indeed was bent and made it appear that the star was closer to the sun when it actually was further away from the disk.

[14] Judah Cohen, "Bundle Up, It's Global Warming," *New York Times*, December 25, 2010, http://www.nytimes.com/2010/12/26/opinion/26cohen.html.

[15] Popper, *Conjectures and Refutations*.

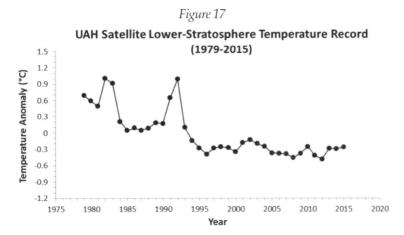

Figure 17

UAH Satellite Lower-Stratosphere Temperature Record (1979-2015)

Note: Lower stratospheric temperatures from the MSU satellites. The two peaks are the result of El Chichón's eruption in 1982 and Mt. Pinatubo's in 1991. The much-reduced cooling after 1995 coincides with the absence of lower atmospheric warming shown earlier in the Remote Sensing System's satellite data, as well as with the pause in surface temperature warming.[16]

Simply put, science that purports to explain everything really explains nothing. That's because it can't be falsified. If stars closest to the sun's limb did not appear to move due to the gravitational lensing effect, then there would be serious problems with Einstein's theory of general relativity. Such a finding would require revision of a great deal (if not all) of the theory because a difficult hypothesis had not been supported in an elegant experimental test.

Lower stratospheric cooling qualifies as one of the difficult predictions of greenhouse warming theory.

Greenhouse warming doesn't fail the test of stratospheric cooling—after all, there is a statistically significant decline in temperature.

But neither does it pass with flying colors. The theory predicts that it should occur at a fairly constant rate. But as is obvious from the satellite data, it occurs in fits and starts, with rapid cooling following major volcanic eruptions (or those few sufficiently powerful to inject a lot of ash and gas into the stratosphere). The

[16] John R. Christy, Roy W. Spencer, and William B. Norris, "The Role of Remote Sensing in Monitoring Global Bulk Tropospheric Temperatures," *International Journal of Remote Sensing* 32 (2011): 671–85.

recent big ones were El Chichón (1982) and Mt. Pinatubo (1991). (For reference, see Figure 17.)

Most interesting of all is the major slowdown in stratospheric cooling that begins in the late 1990s. What is going on above Earth's surface to cause that? Its concurrence with the major slowdown in lower atmospheric (and surface) warming (or the pause) is both suggestive and intriguing.

Greenhouse warming marginally passes the difficult test of stratospheric cooling. Lukewarmers find this to be interesting, as it may be another indicator that estimates of the sensitivity of temperature to carbon dioxide simply are too high.

❧❧❧

17. Popper vs. Knobs on the Climate Machine: Lukewarmers Choose Popper

Global warming can mean colder, it can mean drier, it can mean wetter.

—Steve Guilbeault*

Everybody in the eastern United States has heard this chestnut: "It's not the heat; it's the humidity." The global warming adage is similar—it's not the heat; it's the sensitivity.

Sensitivity represents the amount of warming ultimately projected at the Earth's surface due to a doubling of atmospheric carbon dioxide—nominally a change in concentration from 300 parts per million (ppm) to 600 ppm.

The reality is that the background concentration (often referred to as the "preindustrial" value) is around 0.00028 percent or 280 ppm (which rounds to 300 ppm, for convenience). The current concentration is around 400 ppm (0.00040 percent). These low numbers are why it's called a "trace gas." So we're somewhere around 40 percent higher than what should more appropriately be referred to as the "post-ice-age, pre-industrial baseline."

Other trace greenhouse gases also are increasing. Methane, putatively from bovine flatulence and rice paddy agriculture, is one. Methane adds an equivalent of 10 percent to carbon dioxide's 40 percent. Those evil chlorofluorocarbons (CFCs) are good for another 4 percent. There are a few others, but they're extremely minor. All in all, it's reasonable to say we've gone a bit over halfway to an effective doubling in the atmospheric concentration of CO_2.

But brace yourself: things are about to get very cloudy.

The mean sensitivity of the 108 climate models or runs in the Intergovernmental Panel on Climate Change's (IPCC) latest climate compendium (2013) is 3.2°C (5.8°F). Simple calculations

* Steve Guilbeault is a Canadian science and environmental reporter.

Figure 18

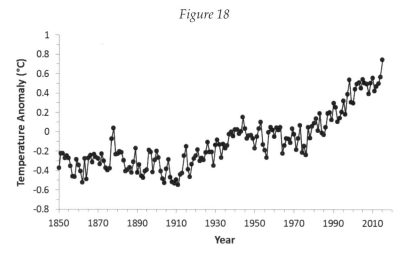

Note: Surface temperature departures from an arbitrary mean in the latest iteration of the University of East Anglia Climate Research Unit compilation. Data through 2015.[1]

made by the Swedish scientist Svante Arrhenius in 1896 suggest we should have seen around 1.4°C (2.5°F) by now. The same number results from calculations utilizing complicated computer models a century later. But, at best, we've seen about 0.6°C (1.1°F) under the (very) liberal assumption that three-fourths of the observed warming is from elevated CO_2.[2]

Figure 18 displays the surface temperature history from the University of East Anglia's Climate Research Unit. This is one that scientists tend to believe more than others. This is noteworthy, despite the fact that there is a new and ongoing investigation into how the original data that form these records have been (favorite word alert) *homogenized*.[3]

There are two warmings. One takes place from about 1910–1945, the second from around 1976–1998. While they are statistically indistinguishable in terms of rate, the first could have little or nothing to

[1] Colin P. Morice et al., "Quantifying Uncertainties," and updates.

[2] We personally believe the fraction to be about half rather than three-quarters.

[3] Global Warming Policy Foundation, "Inquiry Launched into Global Temperature Data Integrity," April 25, 2015, http://www.thegwpf.org /?s =%3A++Inquiry+Launched+into+Global+Temperature+Data+Integrity.

do with greenhouse gas changes because the developed world didn't really crank up its emissions until World War II. The warming since then works out to 0.6°C (1.4°F), or less than half of what it should be if one accepts the UN's mean climate model sensitivity.

As a consequence, the high-sensitivity models need something to bring them into accord with observed reality. That "something" literally can be seen in Beijing, China, where the air often is opaque. Although there are many causes for Beijing's miasmatic environment, the number one factor has been China's growing economy, one that largely runs on unscrubbed, coal-fired power plants and manufacturing facilities.

Everyone knows that cities tend to be warmer than the surrounding countryside. Buildings retain heat at night. Their height impedes ventilating winds. Black pavement heats up like a nun's habit in August. Air conditioners in the process of chilling indoor air return the heat they extract to the outside environment. The result is an urban heat island effect that often confounds efforts to accurately measure average surface temperature. Great care must be taken in accounting for the urban heat island effect. Some say not enough care has been taken.

China is the only place on earth where cities are so polluted with sun-blocking aerosols that some of them have shown an "urban cool island effect" thanks to all the junk in the air.

It was 1987 when Tom Wigley, serving as director of the University of East Anglia Climatic Research Unit, first conceded that something was wrong with the models his organization was circulating.[4]

By 1995, the IPCC was onboard:

> When increases in greenhouse gases only are taken into account . . . most GCMs [climate models] produce a greater mean warming than has been observed, unless a lower climate sensitivity is used. . . . There is growing evidence that increases in sulfate aerosols are partially counteracting the [warming] due to increases in greenhouse gases.

The fix for the difference between the models' output and observed reality was to extend the cooling effect of industrial aerosols—mainly sulfate chips—from China out to the world at large.

---

[4] The Climate Research Unit at the University of East Anglia published this in its in-house journal, *Climate Monitor*.

But no one knows what the myriad effects of sulfate aerosols are. For example, many aerosols are black and preferentially absorb solar radiation. This seemingly would provide some counteraction of their cooling effect. Some aerosols serve as tiny nuclei around which water vapor molecules coalesce and condense. This effect might enhance rainfall, but that's getting us into the very complicated and poorly understood effect of clouds on large regions of Earth's surface, and even global climate.

As a consequence, when the important question is asked, "How much do the aerosols counteract greenhouse warming?" scientists respond with a very large range of possibility. The 2013 IPCC report estimates that the potential temperature effects range from –0.1°C to –1.4°C (–0.2°F to –2.6°F). This essentially means that any value able to accommodate the observed temperature history can be plugged into a computer model—sort of like what happens in Popperian pseudoscience.

If your model has a high sensitivity and is predicting the present temperature should be hotter than a modern ballpark seat on a sunny July day, inputting a large amount of aerosol cooling will fix that. If your model has a low sensitivity, you are free to choose a low aerosol figure.

Lukewarmers are very skeptical of models that can be tuned in order to mimic any version of the past. As Popper showed, science that is consistent with everything isn't science at all because it can't be tested. The enormous range of cooling that can be inserted into the model assumptions renders them useless. However, if that range were to be narrowed, we might be able to converge upon a more confident prediction for future warming.

Bjorn Stevens heads a premier climate research group at the Max Planck Institute for Meteorology in Hamburg, Germany. If his results hold up (and there are many reasons to believe they will), he may prove to have published the most important climate paper in decades on the effects of sulfate aerosols.[5]

As noted, the global temperature history contains two periods of warming. The first occurs between 1910 and 1945, when carbon dioxide emissions aren't likely to have had much effect because the

---

[5] Bjorn Stevens, "Rethinking the Lower Bound on Aerosol Radiative Forcing," *Journal of Climate* 28 (2015): 4794–819.

Figure 19

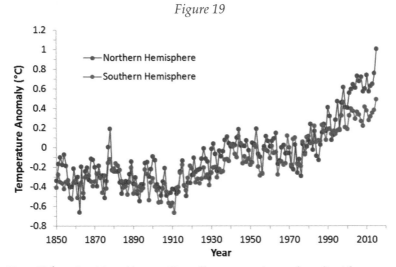

Note: If there is a big sulfate cooling effect countering carbon dioxide warming, (1) the clean Southern Hemisphere should behave much differently from the dirty Northern Hemisphere over the entire record—which isn't the case, and (2) the models will greatly underestimate the warming of the dirty early 20th century—which they do. The 2015 El Niño spike is rather obvious.[6]

period predates World War II, when the vast majority of emissions began. One piece of evidence for this is that the climate models don't pick up the first warming at all unless they are properly "tuned." But Stevens cleverly picked up what this failure really means—tuning the models to detect the early warming renders unrealistic results when more recent decades are closely examined.

As noted, sulfate aerosols are a very common form of pollution. Their largest source is the combustion of coal. Because of coal's heavy use there could not have been a great cleaning of the atmosphere in the early 20th century. To the contrary, the sulfate load was growing by leaps and bounds. Additionally, the vast majority of the developed world's prewar overland freight was moved by coal-fired steam engines, dispersing sulfate aerosols everywhere they went.

Stevens took advantage of this insight and a few other anomalies that would constrain the range of cooling from sulfate aerosols. Almost all the world's sulfate aerosols are emitted in the Northern

[6] Colin P. Morice et al., "Quantifying Uncertainties," and updates.

Hemisphere. This is because there hardly is any industry—and precious little electricity generation using coal (or any electricity at all)—in vast swaths of the Southern Hemisphere. Therefore, Stevens reasons, if sulfates are holding down global temperature, they must exert their maximum influence in the Northern Hemisphere. As a corollary, the Southern Hemisphere should have been warming smartly in recent years due to their absence. Figure 19 shows that this is not the case.

Stevens shows that the models can't get the warming of the early 20th century right because their sulfate cooling simply is far too large—which means the models must have an unrealistically high sensitivity to carbon dioxide, just as lukewarmers have been saying for years.

After all is said and done, Stevens whittles down the sulfate cooling effect and estimates it to be from 0.2°C (0.4°F) to 0.8°C (1.4°F). Nic Lewis, an independent researcher who publishes on the subject of sensitivity along with Georgia Institute of Technology's Judith Curry, has examined the statistics in Stevens's work and concludes that the most likely value for the effect of sulfates is to exert a cooling of 0.4°C (0.7°F), which is *less than half* as much cooling as they exert in most of the IPCC's models.[7]

Lukewarmers have long suspected that sulfate cooling was overblown when used to correct overheated models.[8]

---

[7] Nicholas Lewis and Judith A. Curry, "The Implications for Climate Sensitivity of AR5 Forcing and Heat Uptake Estimates," *Climate Dynamics* 45 (2015): 1009–23.

[8] Patrick J. Michaels et al., "General Circulation Models: Testing the Forecast," *Technology: Journal of the Franklin Institute* 331A (1994): 123–33.

18. Does This Tail Make Me Look Fat?

The data don't matter. We're not basing our recommendations
[for reductions in carbon dioxide emissions] upon the data.
We're basing them upon the climate models.

—Chris Folland*

People fear fat tails. Fortunately, they're hard to find in a lukewarm world.

In this case, "tail" refers to the end of a probability distribution.
Climate models that have a drawn-out, rightward (warm) tail raise
the specter that the probability of a high-end warming of, say, 6°C in
little more than a century isn't too low to not worry about.[1] Figure 20
shows the probability distribution for different amounts of warming taken from various models in the 2007 Intergovernmental Panel
on Climate Change (IPCC) report (the analogous figure in the most
recent, 2013, report isn't as clear, even as it shows many of the same
models).

Georgia Tech's Nic Lewis plowed through Bjorn Stevens's numbers
and posted his findings on Judith Curry's blog, *Climate Etc.* (http://
www.judithcurry.com), which is worth reading regularly even if you
must put up with the fact that it's a strong attractor for wonks.

The Lewis and Curry paper in *Climate Dynamics* mentioned in
the last chapter compares the recent past against four different
base periods. A shorter time between a base period and the present

---

*Chris Folland works part time on seasonal forecasting and seasonal to multi-
decadal climate variability and as an adviser to the Met Office in the Hadley Centre
(UK). He was coordinating lead author of the UN Intergovernmental Panel on Climate
Change's 1990 report and lead author of the 1998 report. As a lead author, he shares in
the Nobel Prize awarded the IPCC in 2007.

[1] Readers will know why we use the cognate "high-end" rather than the more common word "disastrous" by the time this book gets to our discussion of the situation
in Greenland.

Figure 20

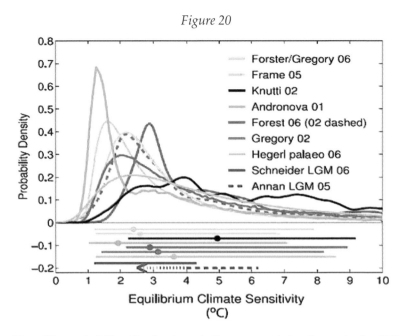

Note: The probability distribution of climate sensitivity shown in the 2007 IPCC report has fat tails for high-end warming.[2]

obviously contains more reliable estimates of aerosols and temperature than a base period back in the 18th century. It is somewhat reassuring that their sensitivity estimates are quite indifferent to the length of the base period they use.

Lewis reran his and Curry's analysis on Judith's blog using the new aerosol results found in Stevens's paper. It paints a very pretty picture indeed, with tails that appear to have been on a Slim-Fast diet. It's a picture that is dramatically different from what the IPCC paints.

The sensitivity that usually is shown is called the "equilibrium sensitivity" because it's the total amount of warming for doubling carbon dioxide with no additional increase in its concentration

[2] S. Solomon et al., eds., *Climate Change 2007: The Physical Science Basis. Contribution of Working Group I to the Fourth Assessment Report of the Intergovernmental Panel on Climate Change* (New York: Cambridge University Press, 2007).

Figure 21

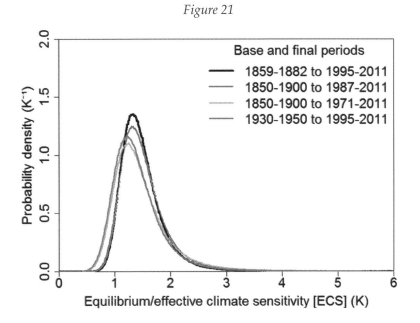

Note: Probability of different amounts of warming for doubling CO_2 after the atmosphere comes to equilibrium, using the sulfate cooling distribution in Stevens's paper.[3]

(Figures 20 and 21). As such, it's a kind of theoretical thing that is unlikely to be seen because in the real world the CO_2 concentration likely will not be static after the point at which it doubles. There's another, perhaps more useful, type of sensitivity that differs from what we are showing here. It's called "transient sensitivity," which is the realized temperature change at the time of doubling. Under the IPCC's midrange scenario, we get to a doubling somewhere around 2065.

Lewis uses Stevens's sulfate cooling estimates to calculate the transient as well (Figure 22). The most likely value is a net warming

[3] Nicholas Lewis, "The Implications for Climate Sensitivity of Bjorn Stevens's New Aerosol Forcing Paper," a guest post on Steve McIntyre's blog *Climate Audit*, March 19, 2015, at 4:44 p.m., http://climateaudit.org/2015/03/19/the-implications-for-climate-sensitivity-of-bjorn-stevens-new-aerosol-forcing-paper/.

Figure 22

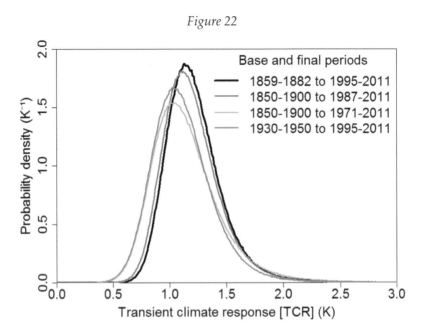

Note: Probability distribution for warming at the time of effective CO_2 doubling, or around 2065 in the IPCC's midrange emissions scenario, again as calculated by Nic Lewis using data in Stevens's 2015 paper.[4]

of 1.2°C (2.2°F). If one assumes that 0.6°C (1.1°C) of the presently observed warming is a result of enhanced greenhouse gases, this means we can expect an additional 0.6°C over the next 50 years—or a warming rate of a mere 0.12°C (0.22°F) per decade. If we more realistically attribute half of the observed warming (0.4°C) to pernicious economic activity, then the rate from now until 2065 becomes 0.16°C (0.29°F) per decade, or the same average decadal warming that has been experienced since the mid-1970s (Figure 23).

Lukewarmers know a weak sulfate effect is the death knell for fat tails.

[4] Ibid.

Figure 23

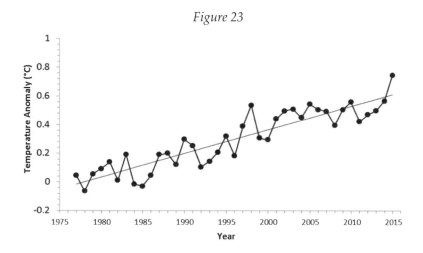

Note: Despite the pause, the constant warming rate of 0.16°C (0.29°F) per decade fits the climate's behavior since the mid-1970s, when the second warming of the 20th century commenced. It fits the data very well. It also perfectly fits Nic Lewis's transient calculation, applicable to around 2065.[5]

[5] Colin P. Morice et al., "Quantifying Uncertainties."

19. Some More Insensitivity about Global Warming

> There's also reluctance [to acknowledge the low-sensitivity model], I'm sure, because the recent work is trending toward the published low sensitivity findings from a decade ago from climate scientists best known for their relationships with libertarian groups.
>
> —Andrew Revkin*

Because they're much like other people, lukewarmers view themselves as eminently reasonable. Probably in order to preserve their sanity, they believe that there will come a day when the high-sensitivity paradigm collapses under its own weight. That collapse may have begun four years ago.

Beginning in 2011, an increasing number of papers arguing for a low sensitivity began to appear. They don't generate much discussion in the paradigm-defining documents of the Intergovernmental Panel on Climate Change (IPCC) or U.S. Global Change Research Program. If they are mentioned at all, it's likely to be dismissively. Nonetheless there are plenty of such research papers by some pretty prestigious authors.

For example, in 2011, Richard Lindzen—former Alfred P. Sloan professor of meteorology at the Massachusetts Institute of Technology and a Cato Institute distinguished senior fellow—examined discrete warming and cooling periods of the tropical ocean and compared them with changes in outgoing radiation that would be expected with a changing greenhouse effect. Lindzen and his colleague Yong-Sang Choi concluded that the relationship between the

---

*For 15 years, Andrew Revkin was a science and environment reporter before he left the *New York Times* in 2009 to become a senior fellow at Pace University. Revkin continues to write for the *Dot Earth* blog associated with the *Times*'s opinion pages. This quotation is from his February 4, 2013, blog post, "A Closer Look at Moderating Views of Climate Sensitivity," http://dotearth.blogs.nytimes.com/2013/02/04/a-closer-look-at-moderating-views-of-climate-sensitivity/?_r=0.

two implies a lower sensitivity of temperature, or even a negative temperature feedback between tropical ocean warming and subsequent global temperature. In their words, this "implies that the models are exaggerating climate sensitivity."[1]

Andreas Schmittner and his colleagues at Oregon State University use a different approach to get at the sensitivity. They combined large-scale temperature reconstructions from the height of the last ice age with various model simulations (which include changing CO_2) and found a mean sensitivity of 2.3°C (4.1°F). The climate model average sensitivity in the most recent (2013) IPCC compendium is 3.2°C (5.8°F). Perhaps even more important, their findings lop off the fat tail discussed in the previous chapter. They conclude, "Assuming paleoclimatic constraints apply to the future as predicted by our model, these results imply lower probability of imminent extreme climatic change than previously thought."[2]

In another 2011 paper, James Annan of the Japan Agency for Marine-Earth Science and Technology and his colleague J. C. Hargreaves note that the standard methodology used to generate the distributions of probable sensitivities "has unacceptable properties" that make it produce unrealistically high probabilities for large warming. By using a more realistic approach, the 95 percent confidence limit for a large warming drops by one-third. They note, "These results also impact strongly on projected economic losses due to climate change." They found a median value for the equilibrium climate sensitivity of 1.9°C (3.4°F) or 2.2°C (4.0°F) for different techniques applied to the same data.[3]

One of the most important low-sensitivity papers was published in 2012 by Michael J. Ring and his coauthors, among whom is University of Illinois's flamboyant Michael Schlesinger. Schlesinger long has been an extremely vocal advocate for a high-end sensitivity. By adjusting their model with observed temperatures (which largely include the pause), Ring and his colleagues arrived at a sensitivity of

---

[1] Richard S. Lindzen and Yong-Sang Choi, "On the Observational Determination of Climate Sensitivity and Its Implications," *Asia-Pacific Journal of Atmospheric Science* 47 (2011): 377–90.

[2] Andreas Schmittner et al., "Climate Sensitivity Estimated from Temperature Reconstructions of the Last Glacial Maximum," *Science* 334 (2011): 1385–88.

[3] J. D. Annan and J. C. Hargreaves, "On the Generation and Interpretation of Probabilistic Estimates of Climate Sensitivity," *Climatic Change* 104 (2011): 423–36.

1.5–2.0°C. Nonetheless, ever mindful to protect the IPCC, they claim that this is "on the low end of the estimates in the [2007] IPCC's Fourth Assessment Report." It is, in fact, clearly beneath the IPCC 2007 value.[4]

Hans van Hateren, at the University of Groningen in the Netherlands, also notes (using a retrospective approach), "The sensitivity was likely . . . lower than [the IPCC's] best estimate [3°C, range 2–4.5°C]." In this he, too, was referring to the 2007 IPCC report.[5]

Each of these results indicates reasonable people have good reasons to doubt the IPCC consensus on warming.

J. C. Hargreaves and fellow researchers in 2012 used the difference between temperatures at the height of the last ice age and conditions today to derive estimates of the climate sensitivity. Using two different statistical methods, they found the same result—a mean equilibrium climate sensitivity of about 2.5°C (4.5°F) with a 90 percent confidence range of about 1°C to 4°C (1.8°F–7.2°F). This result is much more narrow than what one finds in the collection of papers from the 2007 IPCC report (see Chapter 18, Figure 20).[6]

One of the most interesting low-sensitivity papers is by Roy Spencer and William Braswell in 2014. They modeled the global ocean temperature response and sequentially added different factors to the model (e.g., volcanoes, greenhouse gases, and El Niños). Then they interacted changes in cloudiness associated with El Niños.[7]

Comparing real-world observations always is a good idea in science, and the technique Spencer and Braswell employ allows them to determine the sensitivity of temperature to doubled CO_2. They found that the best match between their model and reality occurred with a sensitivity of 1.3°C (3.0°F). Climate models that fail to accurately recognize the El Niño cloud feedback produce sensitivities far in excess of this sort of observationally determined one. Perhaps this is yet another explanation for the prevalence of hot models. Most

[4] Michael J. Ring et al., "Causes of the Global Warming Observed since the 19th Century," *Atmospheric and Climate Sciences* 2 (2012): 401–15.

[5] J. H. van Hateren, "A Fractal Climate Response Function Can Simulate Global Average Temperature Trends of the Modern Era and the Past Millennium," *Climate Dynamics* 40 (2013): 2651–70.

[6] Julia C. Hargreaves et al., "Can the Last Glacial Maximum Constrain Climate Sensitivity?" *Geophysical Research Letters* 39 (2012): L24702.

[7] Roy W. Spencer and William D. Braswell, "The Role of ENSO in Global Ocean Temperature Changes during 1955–2011 Simulated with a 1D Climate Model," *Asia-Pacific Journal of Atmospheric Sciences* 50 (2014): 229–37.

climate simulations either don't produce El Niños or the ones they do produce are very unrealistic. Critics have accused some of the modelers of thriving mainly in a data-free environment.

There are many other low-sensitivity papers. Many (but not all) are incorporated into Figure 24. Perhaps the most interesting among them is a 2013 analysis by Alexander Otto and a host of colleagues. Fifteen of the 17 also were lead authors in preparing the 2013 IPCC report, mostly in the climate modeling sections. In other words, the 15 coauthors are the very people who largely are responsible for writing that chapter.[8]

Otto (who is at the University of Oxford) and his coauthors acknowledge both the pause in temperature rise and the uptake of heat by the ocean. They note that these imply a lower sensitivity than has been found in previous models. Using more precise radiation data collected over recent years, they calculate a 5–95 percent confidence range of 1.2–3.9°C (2.1–7.0°F) and a mean sensitivity that is more than 40 percent less than the average characterized in the 2013 IPCC report. Yet, somehow, the paradigm of dramatic warming remains intact.

This prompts a serious question: if so many of the scientists who are credited alongside Otto in this research also are authors of the IPCC report, how on our getting-greener Earth could that report still contain the higher sensitivity unless the IPCC leadership is wed to a predetermined result?

Figure 24 summarizes these low-sensitivity papers. Note that they first begin appearing in 2011. There is an important exception among them, one that was one of the repeated topics in the now infamous Climategate emails. Our figure summarizes the results of 17 studies describing at least 25 separate simulations of the sensitivity, as carried out by 50 scientists.[9]

---

[8] Alexander Otto et al., "Energy Budget Constraints on Climate Response," *Nature Geoscience* 6 (2013): 415–16.

[9] "Climategate" refers to the unauthorized November 17, 2009, release of more than 1,000 emails from the server at the Climate Research Unit of the University of East Anglia. The emails revealed repeated attempts by a large community of climate researchers and other scientists to ignore inconvenient data, to evade requests for raw climate data, and to vilify journal editors who published low-sensitivity papers or others that indicated that the current warm era is not without precedent in the past 1,000 years. The specific paper to which we are referring is our own from 2002 and was published in the journal *Climate Research*. Our publication precedes by nearly a decade the other papers referenced in this chapter. The exchange of emails that came to light clearly shows an effort to remove the editor who had approved its publication.

Figure 24

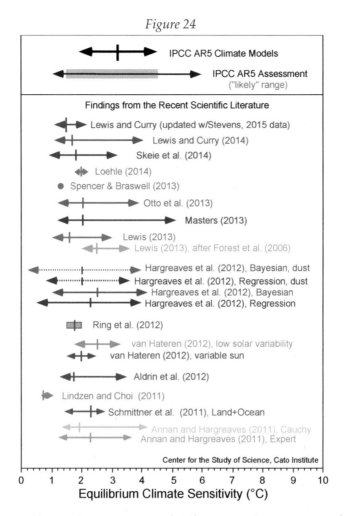

Note: Equilibrium climate sensitivity (ECS) estimates from new research beginning in 2011 (in color) compared with the assessed range provided in the IPCC Fifth Assessment Report (AR5) and the collection of climate models it utilized. The likely (or greater than 66 percent likelihood of occurrence) range in AR5 is indicated by the gray bar. Arrows capture the 5–95 percent confidence bounds for each estimate along with the best estimate (the median of each probability density function or the mean of multiple estimates) as a colored vertical line. Ring et al. (2012) present four estimates of the climate sensitivity. The red box encompasses those four estimates.

The right-hand side of the AR5 range actually is the 90 percent upper bound (the IPCC does not actually state the value for the upper 95 percent confidence bound of its estimate). Spencer and Braswell (2013) produce a single equilibrium climate sensitivity (ECS) value best matched to ocean heat content observations and internal radiative forcing.[10]

While the studies in Figure 24 date from 2011, there are two others that are very similar but were published a decade earlier in 2001 and 2002. They looked at separate lines of evidence indicating the forecasts in 2001's third IPCC assessment used to forecast 21st century warming were far too warm.[11, 12]

Richard Lindzen's paper was in many ways a progenitor of Spencer and Braswell's work in 2013, as we described it earlier. It calculated a much lower sensitivity, as a consequence of satellite evidence that changes in cloud cover compensate, in part, for the warming associated with an El Niño. We used that work—as well as new research on the direct warming that occurs with the emissions of black carbon (soot) into the atmosphere and some new work on CO_2 uptake—to calculate a 2000–2100 warming of 1.9°C (3.4°F). That range turns out to be very close to the actual sensitivity and is very similar to the average of the sensitivity estimates depicted in Figure 24.

[10] The following citations included in our illustration are not mentioned in the text:

(1) Magne Aldrin et al., "Bayesian Estimation of Climate Sensitivity Based on a Simple Climate Model Fitted to Observations of Hemispheric Temperatures and Global Ocean Heat Content," *Environmetrics* 23 (2012): 252–71.

(2) Nicholas Lewis, "An Objective Bayesian Improved Approach for Applying Optimal Fingerprint Techniques to Estimate Climate Sensitivity," *Journal of Climate* 26 (2013): 7414–29.

(3) Craig Loehle, "A Minimal Model for Estimating Climate Sensitivity," *Ecological Modelling* 276 (2014): 80–84.

(4) Troy Masters, "Observational Estimate of Climate Sensitivity from Changes in the Rate of Ocean Heat Uptake and Comparison to CMIP5 Models," *Climate Dynamics* 42 (2014): 2173–81.

(5) R.B. Skeie et al., "A Lower and More Constrained Estimate of Climate Sensitivity Using Updated Observations and Detailed Radiative Forcing Time Series," *Earth System Dynamics* 5 (2014): 139–175.

[11] Richard S. Lindzen et al., "Does the Earth Have an Adaptive Infrared Iris?" *Bulletin of the American Meteorological Society* 82 (2001): 417–32.

[12] Patrick J. Michaels et al., "Revised 21st Century Temperature Projections," *Climate Research* 23 (2002): 1–9. This is the paper that Andrew Revkin refers to in his *DotEarth* blog and that we used as the epigraph to this chapter.

We wrote, "The constancy of these somewhat independent results encourages us to conclude that 21st century warming will be modest and near the low end of the IPCC TAR [Third Assessment Report] projections."

20. The Sociology of Climate Alarmism

> Large-scale hog producers are a greater threat to the United States and U.S. democracy than Osama bin Laden and his terrorist network.
>
> —Robert F. Kennedy Jr.*

Why is it taking so long for climate scientists to let go of the fat tail? The answer might lie in the nature of modern science.

Michael Polanyi (1891–1976) was a 20th-century chemist and philosopher who recognized the horrors of government intervention in science and the pernicious influence of central planning. He argued that science should be considered a free market with spontaneous order, a perspective akin to that of F. A. Hayek (1899–1992), Ludwig von Mises (1881–1973), and other libertarian favorites. Thomas Kuhn (1922–96), a physicist and a philosopher who attended several of Polanyi's lectures, went him one better and argued in his classic *The Structure of Scientific Revolutions* that the order created paradigms, or encompassing philosophical structures, that lie at the core of science.[1]

Within such a paradigm—whether it be in Newtonian physics (which turned out to be a special case of the more encompassing paradigm of Einsteinian physics), the atomic model of chemistry, the central dogma of life orchestrated by nucleic acids, or that of disastrous global warming—the practitioners of science are rewarded and advanced precisely for their ability to shore up the paradigm. But the fact is that most paradigms eventually fail and fall. The concept of a flat earth is an obvious example.

Scientists are rewarded for working within the paradigm rather than for challenging it, even as it may be failing in its explanatory power. In climate change (and other fields in which there are major policy implications), reigning paradigms are often explicitly defined.

---

* Kennedy is Robert F. and Ethel Kennedy's third child, an environmental attorney and activist, and host of the independently syndicated radio program, "Ring of Fire."

[1] Thomas Kuhn, *The Structure of Scientific Revolutions* (Chicago: University of Chicago Press, 1962).

The U.S. Global Change Research Program (USGCRP) is required, by law, to produce a report every five years that summarizes the impact of climate change on the United States. The UN's Intergovernmental Panel on Climate Change (IPCC) produces analogous reports on a global scale every six years.[2]

The overarching climate change paradigm is not defined by observations. Rather, it is defined by computer models. The cornerstone of the 2013 IPCC report is a family of 108 climate models (or model runs) that yield a mean sensitivity of 3.2°C (5.8°F). As the IPCC stated in its 1995 report, left to their own devices, the models produce much more warming than is being observed. Either the sensitivity is wrong or the warming is being largely interfered with by sulfate aerosols.[3]

As we've seen, the work by Stevens and Lewis pretty much disposes of the concept of a large sulfate cooling resulting in a lowered sensitivity. So, why did the sulfate paradigm last so long?

Will Stevens's work and that of many others, as we detailed in the previous chapter, finally bring it down?

Kuhn provides us with his paradigm:

> In science . . . novelty emerges only with difficulty, manifested by resistance, against a background provided by expectation. Initially, only the anticipated and the usual are experienced even under circumstances where anomaly is later to be observed.[4]

Climate science is stuck in this first stage of resistance despite ever-increasing evidence that the sensitivity is too high.

Kuhn began his work on *The Structure of Scientific Revolutions* as a Harvard fellow in 1948. James Conant, Harvard's president and an eminent chemist (and also one of the directors of the Manhattan Project that resulted in the atomic bomb), urged him on. Many scientists believed the bomb project to be a one-off effort. But President Franklin D. Roosevelt didn't. When, in 1944, it became clear that the war would be won, Roosevelt wrote to Vannevar Bush, who was

[2] The reference is to the Global Change Research Act of 1990. The portion of the law requiring summary reports on the impacts of climate change in the United States curiously was set aside during the administration of President George W. Bush. No national assessment of climate change was produced during his tenure.

[3] Bert Bolin et al., *IPCC Second Assessment Climate Change 1995: A Report of the Intergovernmental Panel on Climate Change* (Geneva: IPCC, 1995).

[4] Kuhn, *The Structure of Scientific Revolutions*, p. 64.

100

running the wartime Office of Scientific Research and Development (which oversaw the Manhattan Project), and asked if Bush could provide a plan to keep the large community of scientists in the service of the federal government. Bush grasped the opportunity and shortly afterward penned *Science, the Endless Frontier: A Report to the President*. It served as the blueprint for the federalization of science and provided the framework for what was to become the National Science Foundation.[5]

Bush's proposal became popular largely because Americans believe that scientific research is a public good—something that is right for the public (U.S. taxpayers) to support—and, as the myth goes, science otherwise would wither and die. But Cato Institute adjunct scholar Terence Kealey, having recently stepped down after 14 years service as vice-chancellor (or "president" in the U.S. academic context) of the University of Buckingham (UK), tested that hypothesis. He found there actually to be very little to support it based upon economic data gathered from around the world.[6]

In any case, Bush's proposal was revolutionary and a guarantee that academia would come to addict itself to government welfare. Rather than having the government simply hire individual scientists, Bush's idea was that universities would contract with government to perform research proposed by their faculty. In doing so, they could charge overhead—usually 50 percent (or more) above the original value. This was presumed to help keep the lights on and the university research laboratories warm or—in the case of Stanford University president Donald Kennedy—pay for paneling the university's yacht, silk sheets for a (literally) feathered bed, and the cost of a mansion in which to hold his wedding reception.[7, 8]

---

[5] Vannevar Bush, *Science, the Endless Frontier: A Report to the President* (Washington, D.C.: Government Printing Office, 1945).

[6] Terence Kealey, *The Economic Laws of Scientific Research* (New York: St. Martin's Press, 1996).

[7] Kennedy, after some very embarrassing congressional hearings, resigned and subsequently was named editor-in-chief of *Science*—the flagship journal and newsmagazine of the American Association for the Advancement of Science. That appointment made him the gatekeeper for perhaps the most influential science periodical on Earth. So it goes.

[8] David Folkenflik, "What Happened to Stanford's Expense Scandal?" *Baltimore Sun*, November 20, 1994, http://articles.baltimoresun.com/1994-11-20/news/1994324051_1_stanford-incidental-expenses-auditors.

In other words, because overhead is money, it's fungible. If a school's department of Germanic languages has insufficient student traffic to pay for its faculty and buildings, perhaps some of the university's research overhead will wind up there. Or maybe it will go toward women's studies if the dean thinks they need a few new computers. All of this tends to make the universities and their faculty cheerleaders for all things big-government, or at least it assures that more libertarian faculty are shunned and maybe not even invited to potlucks with the grad students. Too bad!

President Dwight Eisenhower realized that serious unintended consequences could flow from Bush's proposed academic power grab. In his 1961 Farewell Address, given a year before Kuhn's book was published, Eisenhower expressed serious concern. "The prospect of domination of the nation's scholars by Federal employment, project allocations, and the power of money is ever present—and is gravely to be regarded," he said. Eisenhower had gained his experience firsthand as president of Columbia University.

Kuhn seemed oddly oblivious to how a federal takeover of science would influence his paradigmatic model. In climate change, the high-sensitivity paradigm literally is the reason the high-sensitivity paradigm exists. A low-sensitivity paradigm fails to justify the multibillion dollar USGCRP and obviates the requirement for that particular federal conglomerate to summarize global climate change impacts on the United States every five years. The invitation to a conflict of interest seems obvious. The agencies that compose the USGCRP hardly could be expected to lobby for their own demise. Nor are they likely to acknowledge major problems with their high-sensitivity paradigm.

It can come as no surprise that the agencies involved will fail to lobby and testify before Congress concerning discovery of a serious problem with their paradigm. There simply is no incentive for them to do so and there is a very powerful incentive for them to drone on about inevitable gloom and doom.

A low-sensitivity approach will not fund the horde of scientists who receive federal support. And when those individuals peer-review one another's scientific manuscripts, they can be expected to perceive papers that argue for lower sensitivity as threatening the funding stream. As a consequence, low-sensitivity research results generally receive vigorous review while those arguing for high sensitivity and large societal impacts are treated just the opposite.

There is an additional problem that comes when the USGCRP or the IPCC summarizes the available scientific literature in their periodic reviews. The literature is biased to begin with. After all, the USGCRP finds itself largely summarizing a body of scientific literature generated using money the USGCRP disburses to the research community—funding that is dependent upon adherence to the high-sensitivity paradigm. Monopoly federal funding turns Kuhn's paradigms into virtually immobile artifices that provide, in the case of climate change, the sole means for advancement in the academic profession. In the case of the 2013 IPCC report, not one of the 39 models at its core was produced outside of, or without collaboration with, a major government research laboratory.[9]

This framework also explains why it has taken so long to seriously challenge the notion of a large sulfate cooling. There are not many people in a position to do so. Nic Lewis is a semiretired financier and not dependent upon federal funds. Judith Curry, another dissenting scientist, discovered a new sense of freedom when she stopped applying for taxpayer dollars—and she began to speak out. The senior author of this book stopped applying for federal funding 20 years ago simply because he knew it to be a waste of time for anyone who is not onboard with the USGCRP's program. Steve McIntyre, who took down a lynchpin of the high-sensitivity paradigm, simply is retired, well-off, and curious.[10, 11]

Lukewarmers accept that the sulfate explanation for the lack of warming initially was a logical attempt (in the sense Kuhn describes) to shore up the high-sensitivity paradigm. But the paradigm became immobile and sessile due to the federal funding stranglehold. To repeat what Eisenhower said, "The prospect of domination of the

---

[9] The IPCC gets to its total of 108 models by using multiple runs of some of the original 39 models using different assumptions.

[10] The reference here is to McIntyre's work on Michael Mann's "hockey stick" temperature reconstruction, which showed 900 years of a dawdling cooling suddenly disrupted by a sharp warming in the 20th century. As a mathematician, McIntyre was able to demonstrate that such a function was the inevitable result of the manner in which the data were treated.

[11] Stephen McIntyre and Ross McKitrick, "Hockey Sticks, Principal Components, and Spurious Significance," *Geophysical Research Letters* 32 (2005): L03710.

nation's scholars by federal employment [and] project allocations . . . is gravely to be regarded."

Is there evidence that what Eisenhower feared may be harming science itself? Stanford University's Daniele Fanelli examined over 5,000 published papers from around the world across many academic disciplines. His stunning 2012 finding, "Negative Results Are Disappearing from Most Disciplines and Countries," says it all. Fanelli documents a systematic increase in the frequency of "positive" findings being published. There is good empirical evidence in support of the notion that publish-or-perish is the "American model" for science—and as more nations adopt it, the more positive results are published.[12]

In a world where scientists answer real questions, this would be impossible. People haven't suddenly become smarter (except perhaps in how to advance in academia). Candidates for promotion in the sciences fundamentally are asked two questions: "What did you publish, and how much taxpayer money did you bring in to support your research?" If an assistant professor under consideration for tenure answers either question insufficiently, he's likely to be looking for another job. It's amazing how many of them wind up on the staff of congressional committees or, better still, programmatic committees for big government agencies like the National Science Foundation.[13]

Research funding is of paramount importance. At a tier-one university, in order for a researcher to publish the requisite number of papers for promotion in, say, the environmental sciences, several million dollars in research funding are needed. Thanks to the magic of overhead, an assistant professor generates about half of that for everyone else. So the search for knowledge has become a search for funding, and funding agencies tend to frown upon negative results.

Can anyone seriously believe that a young researcher will get that kind of funding by approaching federal agencies with a proposal that global warming's future magnitude and effects have been dramatically overforecast? The mere existence of such a proposal

---

[12] Daniele Fanelli, "Negative Results Are Disappearing from Most Disciplines and Countries," *Scientometrics* 90 (2012): 891–904.

[13] For some curious reason, private research support—especially from any industry with a scientific concern—carries much less weight than does government funding in the promotion process.

threatens to derail everyone else's gravy train. It won't get funded and the researcher won't get promoted.

Stanford University's John Ioannidis may have been the first person to detect this systematic illness infecting science when he wrote his 2005 iconoclastic paper, "Why Most Published Research Findings Are False." His thesis is that the demand to publish and get funding is so strong that many studies are designed poorly to force a positive result and rapid publication. In further work with Daniele Fanelli, Ioannidis found that the addition of a single American author to a multiauthored, international paper greatly raises the probability that it will report a positive result.[14, 15]

In 2013, on the eve of his receipt of the Nobel Prize in Physiology or Medicine, Randy Schekman published an op-ed in the *Guardian* (UK), hardly a conservative publication. It was titled "How Journals Like *Nature*, *Cell*, and *Science* Are Damaging Science," and in it he vowed never to send those journals another manuscript. Schekman wrote that publishing in *Nature* and *Science* is a ticket to tenure and enhanced research funding, but that those two magazines—the two most impactful science publications on Earth—gravitate toward flashy science in order to draw attention to themselves. This inflates their "impact factors" (yes, there is such a metric). This happens at the expense of day-to-day-grind science that, though it may be more important, won't land the researcher in front of the cameras on CNN. Knowing this, people gravitate toward flashy fields like global warming at the expense of others and thereby burn our scientific talent for a mess of pottage.

While there is evidence that government-funded climate science is biased (both in its raw form and when it is summarized), the study of how and why such things happen in climate research and in other branches of science long has been verboten territory—especially given the obviously symbiotic relationship between academia and the federal science establishment. Beyond Fanelli and Ioannidis (and the University of Virginia's Brian Nosek), there aren't many people seriously digging into this.

---

[14] John P. A. Ioannidis, "Why Most Published Research Findings Are False," *PLoS Medicine* 2 (2005): e124.

[15] Ioannidis's presence probably encouraged Fanelli to come to Stanford University, too.

How does funding-induced bias become systemic? One function of federal agencies can be to protect a policy. Hence, the USGCRP (as shown in Chapter 21c) stated in its 2014 National Climate Assessment of the impacts of climate change that it was proud to be producing a "deliverable" for the president's "Climate Action Plan." Bias creeps in because what gets funded by an agency goes to support some policy agenda.

It's also important to note that the policy itself never is questioned. Global warming is a problem, period. Therefore, research funds are directed toward studying the problem or defining a method of dealing with it. Research *assumes* the policy matrix rather than evaluating it.

Additionally, agencies thrive on new initiatives. If the military establishment decides that climate change is a threat to national defense, the Pentagon surely will claim that additional revenue and manpower are required to respond. In this way, issues like climate change slowly creep across the entire government.

As Kuhn showed, the paradigmatic nature of science, even if it is not made more sticky by federal money, is conservative. Federal agency policies, programs, and practices often are based on past science, which operated under a specific paradigm. When a paradigm begins to be questioned within the scientific community, there is a danger that the agency simply will continue to fund research under the existing paradigm. In effect, the agency takes a "side" in a scientific controversy rather than working to resolve it. This clearly is what has happened with global warming. Figure 1 in this publication should have been sufficient to change the paradigm concerning the potential for disastrous climate change were there not so much agency inertia in the way.

All of this is tragic. In biomedicine, people suffer and die because of falsely promised cures. In climate change, we get poisonous policies emanating from absurd results generated by climate models that can't even get the past two decades right.

21a. The First National Climate Assessment: Willful Violation of Normative Science

A global climate treaty must be implemented even if there is no scientific evidence to back the greenhouse effect.

—Richard Benedik*

Lukewarmers fear that President Eisenhower was right, that the federal government *intentionally* funds and produces research that will produce a paradigm of extreme climate change and horrible effects. Do they have a legitimate worry?

The Global Change Research Act of 1990 established the U.S. Global Change Research Program (USGCRP) and also mandated its production of periodic "national climate assessments" of climate change. The first such assessment was published in 2000 and was produced by the U.S. National Climate Assessment (NCA) "synthesis team." In order to "assess" future impacts, the NCA needed to employ some type of climate model. The NCA had nine to choose from and it settled on two. One was the Canadian General Circulation Climate Model (CGCM1), which forecast more warming than any other model considered. The other was from Britain's Hadley Center (and called HadCM2). It forecast larger precipitation changes than any of the others.

In a review, we decided to see how well the two models would perform if simply asked to estimate 10-year running averages of U.S. temperature during the 20th century. They performed so poorly that their predictions were statistically worse than merely assuming

---

* Richard Benedik was the chief U.S. negotiator for 1987's Montreal Protocol on Ozone-Depleting Substances.

the mean temperature for the century would be realized for every 10-year sample. That's basically a "no forecast" assumption.

If that seems incredible, it is. The purpose of any model is to help explain the behavior of a particular system. Therefore, the simplest test of any model is whether the difference between the modeled values and actual observations is smaller than the difference between the observations and their overall average. In other words, if a continual forecast of the simple average of observations performs better than the model's predictions, the model is useless. This is exactly what we found in examining the performance of the two models used in the NCA when it came to its ability to predict the evolution of U.S. average temperature over the 20th century. Somehow, employing the climate models resulted in "negative knowledge," a situation totally analogous to supplying students with four choices in a multiple-choice test and their getting less than 25 percent correct.

We sent our peer review to the national assessment team. We told them, in part:

> All implied effects, including the large temperature rise, are therefore based upon a multiple scientific failure. The [NCA's] continued use of those models and that approach is a willful choice to disregard the most fundamental scientific rules (and that they did not find and eliminate such an egregious error is astounding). For that reason alone, the [NCAs] should be withdrawn from the public sphere until it becomes scientifically based.

We also emailed our findings and conclusions to Tom Karl, chairman of the national assessment team. It turns out the synthesis team had run a similar test. Karl responded:

> One has to look at the time averages. In the assessment we were most interested in, decadal to century scale trends, not annual averages [Note: As mentioned above, we used decadal (10-year) moving averages!], so [we] would not be inclined to perform the test you did. . . . Nevertheless we ran the test you did, but changed the averaging period.

He kindly included the results the team looked at: 1-year data and moving averages of 5, 10, 20, and 25 years (Figure 25). At each and

Figure 25

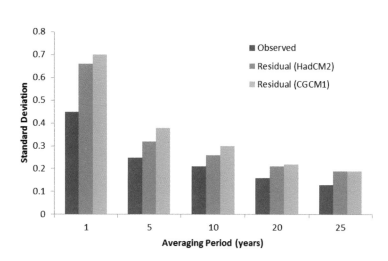

Note: The difference (standard deviation) between the observations and their long-term mean (red bar) is less than the difference (standard deviation) between the model projections and the actual observations (blue bars) throughout all averaging periods using either climate model.[1]

every time scale, the scatter of data was larger after the model was applied. In other words, the model supplied negative knowledge. The team and Karl himself confirmed our finding that the use of both models was worse than using no model at all. Yet the models were retained and drove the findings in the 2000 assessment.

The final report used the same models as the draft report upon which we had commented. The blatant disregard for the norms of science shook our faith and that of many climate scientists. It was instrumental in growing the lukewarm movement.

[1] Adapted from Thomas Karl email correspondence with the author (PJM).

21b. The Second National Climate Assessment: Where's the Rest of the Science?

> Get a good grip on your long johns, cold weather haters—
> the worst may be yet to come. That's the long-long-range
> weather forecast being given out by "climatologists," the
> people who study very long-term world weather trends.
> [quotation marks in original]
>
> —*Washington Post* (January 11, 1970)

Lukewarmers were concerned that the 2000 National Climate Assessment's use of models that were worse than a table of random numbers provided evidence for wholesale scientific corruption in the U.S. Global Change Research Program (USGCRP). The second National Climate Assessment, in 2009, was different. Large tracts of science were summarily ignored, as we noted in our review, which began with this general introduction:[1]

> Of all of the "consensus" government or intergovernmental
> documents of this genre that [we] have reviewed in [our]
> 30+ years in this profession, there is no doubt that this is
> absolutely the worst of all. *Virtually every sentence can be
> contested or does not represent a complete survey of a relevant
> literature.* [emphasis added]

> There is an overwhelming amount of misleading material in
> the CCSP's "Global Climate Change Impacts in the United
> States." It is immediately obvious that the intent of the
> report is not to provide an accurate scientific assessment
> of the current and future impacts of climate change in the
> United States, but to confuse the reader by a loose handling
> of normal climate events (made seemingly more frequent,

---

[1] Michaels, P.J. and P.C. Knappenbeger. "Comments on the Public Review Draft of the Unified Synthesis Product, "Global Climate Change Impacts in the United States", submitted to the U.S. Global Change Research Program, August 20, 2008.

111

intense and damaging simply by our growing population, population movements, and wealth) presented as climate change events. Additionally, there is absolutely no effort made by the CCSP authors to include any dissenting opinion to their declarative statements, despite the peer-reviewed scientific literature being full of legitimate and applicable reports and observations that provide contrasting findings. Yet, quite brazenly, the CCSP authors claim to provide its readers—"U.S. policymakers and citizens"—with the "best available science." This proclamation is simply false.[2]

The uninformed reader   (i.e., the public, reporters, and policymakers) upon reading this report will be [led] to believe that a terrible disaster is soon to befall the United States from human-induced climate change and that almost all of the impacts will be negative and devastating. Of course, if the purpose here is not really to produce an unbiased review of the impact of climate change on the United States, but a political document that will give cover for EPA's decision to regulate carbon dioxide, then there is really no reason to go through the ruse of gathering comments from scientists knowledgeable about the issues, as the only science that is relevant is selected work that fits the authors' pre-existing paradigm.

Could we back up our claim that "virtually every sentence . . . does not represent a complete survey of a relevant literature"?

We assembled a six-person team and proceeded to produce a document designed as an "addendum" to provide what was missing from the original assessment.[3]

[2] The reigning acronym used in this second USGCRP exercise indicates it was produced by the Climate Change Science Program (CCSP). With no wish to deluge our readers with a cascade of changing acronyms describing virtually the same institutions or groups of people, we tend to use USGCRP in place of some entities in this ever-changing, acronym-filled alphabet soup.

[3] The Cato Institute Center for the Study of Science–produced ADDENDUM can be downloaded at http://object.cato.org/pubs/Global-Climate-Change-Impacts.pdf.

Figure 26

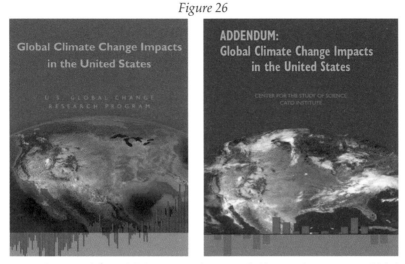

Note: Covers of the USGCRP second National Climate Assessment, *Global Climate Change Impacts in the United States* (left), and the Cato Institute Center for the Study of Science–produced *ADDENDUM: Global Climate Change Impacts in the United States* (right). Curiously, the USGCRP omitted clouds, a major component of climate, and, while showing a map of the United States, included a graphic representing global temperatures. Our addendum shows the past 20 years of U.S. temperature at the time of publication and added some clouds.[4]

Chapter flow and format in our addendum were made as close as possible to those of the second National Climate Assessment. You'll note that the subject matter of each "Key Finding" is the same—only the conclusions differ. Note, too, that as in the assessment, the addendum provides page numbers that reference text in the publication where the basis for a particular finding can be found.

---

[4] Thomas R. Karl et al., *Global Climate Change Impacts in the United States: A State of the Knowledge Report from the U.S. Global Change Research Program* (New York: Cambridge University Press, 2009); Patrick J. Michaels, ed., *ADDENDUM: Global Climate Change Impacts in the United States* (Washington, D.C.: Cato Institute, 2012).

From the second National Climate Assessment:

Key Findings

1. Global warming is unequivocal and primarily human-induced.
Global temperature has increased over the past 50 years. This observed increase is due primarily to human-induced emissions of heat-trapping gases. (p. 13)

2. Climate changes are underway in the United States and are projected to grow.
Climate-related changes are already observed in the United States and its coastal waters. These include increases in heavy downpours, rising temperature and sea level, rapidly retreating glaciers, thawing permafrost, lengthening growing seasons, lengthening ice-free seasons in the ocean and on lakes and rivers, earlier snowmelt, and alterations in river flows. These changes are projected to grow. (p. 27)

3. Widespread climate-related impacts are occurring now and are expected to increase.
Climate changes are already affecting water, energy, transportation, agriculture, ecosystems, and health. These impacts are different from region to region and will grow under projected climate change. (p. 41-106, 107-152)

4. Climate change will stress water resources.
Water is an issue in every region, but the nature of the potential impacts varies. Drought, related to reduced precipitation, increased evaporation, and increased water loss from plants, is an important issue in many regions, especially in the West. Floods and water quality problems are likely to be amplified by climate change in most regions. Declines in mountain snowpack are important in the West and Alaska where snowpack provides vital natural water storage. (p. 41, 129, 135, 139)

5. Crop and livestock production will be increasingly challenged.
Many crops show positive responses to elevated carbon dioxide and low levels of warming, but higher levels of warming often negatively affect growth and yields. Increased pests, water stress, and diseases, and weather extremes will pose adaptation challenges for crop and livestock production. (p. 71)

6. Coastal areas are at increasing risk from sea-level rise and storm surge.
Sea-level rise and storm surge place many U.S. coastal areas at increasing risk of erosion and flooding, especially along the Atlantic and Gulf Coasts, Pacific Islands, and parts of Alaska. Energy and transportation infrastructure and other property in coastal areas are very likely to be adversely affected. (p. 111, 139, 145, 149)

7. Risks to human health will increase.
Harmful health impacts of climate change are related to increasing heat stress, waterborne diseases, poor air quality, extreme weather events, and diseases transmitted by insects and rodents. Reduced cold stress provides some benefits. Robust public health infrastructure can reduce the potential for negative impacts. (p. 89)

8. Climate change will interact with many social and environmental stresses.
Climate change will combine with pollution, population growth, overuse of resources, urbanization, and other social, economic, and environmental stresses to create larger impacts than from any of these factors alone. (p. 99)

9. Thresholds will be crossed, leading to large changes in climate and ecosystems.
There are a variety of thresholds in the climate system and ecosystems. These thresholds determine, for example, the presence of sea ice and permafrost, and the survival of species, from fish to insect pests, with implications for society. With further climate change, the crossing of additional thresholds is expected. (p. 76, 82, 115, 137, 142)

10. Future climate change and its impacts depend on choices made today.
The amount and rate of future climate change depend primarily on current and future human-caused emissions of heat-trapping gases and airborne particles. Responses involve reducing emissions to limit future warming, and adapting to the changes that are unavoidable. (p. 25, 29)

Here are the "Key Findings" from our addendum:

Key Findings

1. Climate change is unequivocal, and human activity plays some part in it.
There are two periods of warming in the 20th century that are statistically indistinguishable in magnitude. The first had little if any relation to changes in atmospheric carbon dioxide, while the second has characteristics that are consistent in part with a changed greenhouse effect. (p. 17)

2. Climate change has occurred and will occur in the United States.
U.S. temperature and precipitation have changed significantly over some states since the modern record began in 1895. Some changes, such as the amelioration of severe winter cold in the northern Great Plains, are highly consistent with a changed greenhouse effect. (pp. 38–56, 187–92)

3. Impacts of observed climate change have little national significance.
There is no significant long-term change in U.S. economic output that can be attributed to climate change. The slow nature of climate progression results in *de facto* adaptation, as can be seen with sea level changes on the East Coast. (pp. 48–49, 79–81, 155–58, 173–74)

4. Climate change will affect water resources.
Long-term paleoclimatic studies show that severe and extensive droughts have occurred repeatedly throughout the Great Plains and the West. These will occur in the future, with or without human-induced climate change. Infrastructure planners would be well-advised to take them into account. (pp. 57–71)

5. Crop and livestock production will adapt to climate change.
There is a large body of evidence that demonstrates substantial untapped adaptability of U.S. agriculture to climate change, including crop-switching that can change the species used for livestock feed. In addition, carbon dioxide itself is likely increasing crop yields and will continue to do so in increasing increments in the future. (pp. 102–18)

6. Sea level rise caused by global warming is easily adapted to.
Much of the densely populated East Coast has experienced sea level rises in the 20th century that are more than twice those caused by global warming, with obvious adaptation. The mean projections from the United Nations will likely be associated with similar adaptation. (pp. 173–74)

7. Life expectancy and wealth are likely to continue to increase.
There is little relationship between climate and life expectancy and wealth. Even under the most dire climate scenarios, people will be much wealthier and healthier in the year 2100 than they are today. (pp. 139–45, 158–61)

8. Climate change is a minor overlay on U.S. society.
People voluntarily expose themselves to climate changes throughout their lives that are much larger and more sudden than those expected from greenhouse gases. The migration of U.S. population from the cold North and East to the much warmer South and West is an example. Global markets exist to allocate resources that fluctuate with the weather and climate. (pp. 154–69)

9. Species and ecosystems will change with or without climate change.
There is little doubt that some ecosystems, such as the desert West, have been changing with climate, while others, such as cold marine fisheries, move with little obvious relationship to climate. (pp. 119–38, 208)

10. Policies enacted by the developed world will have little effect on global temperature.
Even if every nation that has obligations under the Kyoto Protocol agreed to reduce emissions over 80 percent, there would be little or no detectable effect on climate in the policy-relevant timeframe, because emissions from these countries will be dwarfed in coming decades by the total emissions from China, India, and the developing world. (pp. 28, 211)

The second National Climate Assessment illustrates the problems that result when it is in the self-interest of the writers of a scientific compendium (in this case, USGCRP) to perpetuate and enhance their existence. Consequently, the second assessment blatantly disregards a large number of findings, mainly in the literature on plant physiology, ecology, and related fields that show the adaptive nature of Earth's vegetation both to changing climate and higher CO_2 concentrations.

This is different from the meme of distorted science; in this case, it's *ignored* science.

The last half of the 20th century saw two towering figures in plant physiology—Sylvan Wittwer and Paul Waggoner. Both had very long careers and taught a tremendous number of graduate students, who then multiplied the already voluminous work of their mentors throughout their subsequent careers.

Neither man bought into the paradigm of carbon dioxide–induced disaster. They established their reputations and powerful positions long before global warming took over environmental science.

Wittwer was the long-time director of the Michigan State University Agricultural Experiment Station. In the early 1970s, he served as chairman of the Board on Agriculture of the National Research Council. He established himself in these positions because of his reputation as a pioneering scientist whose work in large part established the paradigm that increasing CO_2 would make plants grow better. Wittwer was both long-lived (1917–2012) and productive (over 750 scientific papers). As a result, the field of plant physiology largely resisted the gloom-and-doom that infected so much science. His book, *Food, Climate, and Carbon Dioxide* remains the foundation for the paradigm of a planet that is greening up as CO_2 concentrations increase.[5]

Waggoner was highly influential in agronomy. He directed the prestigious Connecticut Agricultural Experiment Research Station. He too was prolific. Waggoner's work on physical and physiological adaptation of plants to changes in climate and CO_2 enshrined him, like Wittwer, as a leading scientist before the global warming coup. Late in his career, he and New York University's Jesse Ausubel

---

[5] Sylvan Harold Wittwer, *Food, Climate, and Carbon Dioxide* (Boca Raton, FL: CRC Press, 1995).

famously noted the ever-decreasing ecological footprint of individuals in advanced societies.[6]

Their work and that of their intellectual progeny largely was ignored in the second National Climate Assessment. In response to that neglect, our addendum is more highly referenced than the second assessment, especially in the sections on "Agriculture" and "Ecosystems." The addendum has 932 citations. Many are from scientists whose research efforts can be traced to the work of Waggoner and Wittwer before them. The second National Climate Assessment provides 569.

When entire schools of thought on adaption and the response of Earth's vegetation to changing CO_2 and climate are largely ignored, lukewarmers become rightfully suspicious.

99

---

[6] Jesse H. Ausubel and Paul E. Waggoner, "Dematerialization: Variety, Caution, and Persistence," *Proceedings of the National Academy of Sciences* 105 (2008): 12774–79.

21c. The Third National Climate Assessment: "A Key Deliverable of President Obama's Climate Action Plan"

> Creativity in science could be described as the act of putting two and two together to make five.
>
> —Arthur Koestler*

Lukewarmers understand how governments can buy science, but it's actually refreshing when governments frankly admit that the documents their scientists produce are designed to support government policies.

When the National Oceanic and Atmospheric Administration proudly released the third National Climate Assessment—*Climate Change Impacts in the United States*—on May 6, 2014, the agency was pleased to note, "The report, *a key deliverable of President Obama's Climate Action Plan*, is the most comprehensive and authoritative scientific report ever generated about climate changes that are happening now in the United States and further changes that we can expect to see throughout this century" [emphasis added].[1]

While lukewarmers don't find the assessment to be particularly comprehensive, it surely is long at 829 pages plus another 375 pages or so in supplemental material.

As with previous assessments, a draft was sent out for review. This time, on April 15, 2013, we supplied 133 single-spaced pages and summarized our review this way:

> One wonders how familiar the 240 authors of the 2013 draft National Climate Assessment are with Karl Popper's

---

* Arthur Koestler (1905–83) was a Hungarian-British author and journalist.

[1] Jerry M. Melillo et al., eds., *2014: Climate Change Impacts in the United States: The Third National Climate Assessment* (Washington, D.C.: Government Printing Office, 2014).

famous essay on the nature of science and its distinction from "pseudoscience." The essential difference is that science only explains some things and that its hypotheses forbid others, while a theory that is not refutable by any conceivable event (i.e., one that is universally and comprehensively explanatory) is pseudoscience. For Popper, science is characterized by risky predictions (such as gravitational lensing of light in relativity), while pseudoscience does not lend itself to such testing. His favorite examples of pseudoscience were Marxism and Freudian psychology.

This National Climate Assessment is much closer to pseudoscience than it is to science. It is as explanatory as Sigmund Freud. It clearly believes that virtually everything in our society is tremendously dependent on the surface temperature and, because of that, we are headed toward certain and inescapable destruction, unless we take its advice and decarbonize our economy, pronto. Unfortunately, the Assessment can't quite tell us how to accomplish that, because no one knows how.

In the Assessment's 1,200 horror-studded pages, almost everything that happens in our complex world—sex, birth, disease, death, hunger, and wars, to name a few—is somehow made worse by pernicious emissions of carbon dioxide and the joggling of surface average temperature by a mere two degrees.

Virtually every chapter in the Assessment perseverates on extreme weather, despite the U.N. Intergovernmental Panel on Climate Change statement that:

> There is medium evidence and high agreement that long-term trends in normalized losses have not been attributed to natural or anthropogenic climate change.

The Assessment is woefully ignorant of humanity's ability to adapt and prosper in response to challenges. The quintessence of this is the truly dreadful chapter on human health and climate change.

While death, disease, poverty and injustice are all conjured by warming, there is not one mention of the fact that life expectancy in the U.S. is approximately twice what it was in the year 1900, or that per-capita income in constant dollars is over ten times what it was then. It emphasizes diseases that will somehow spread because of warming, neglecting the fact that many were largely endemic when it was colder and were largely eradicated as we warmed a bit.

Further, it conspicuously ignores the fact that doubling the life expectancy of some 200 million Americans who lived in the 20th century is the same as saving 100 million lives. The society that achieved this powered itself on the combustion of fossil fuels. Does this community of experts understand that the number of lives that it effectively saved is orders of magnitude above and beyond what it could possibly cost? It seems, given the panoply of horrors due to start *pronto*, to prefer that we not have emitted carbon dioxide in the first place. Perhaps they ought to look to a place that didn't. Surely part of the $3.5 billion that the US Global Change Research Program (USGCRP) consumes per year could finance a field trip to Chad, so they can see the world without cheap and abundant energy. . . .

[The purpose of the assessment] is to provide cover for a massive regulatory intrusion and concomitant enormous costs in resources and individual liberty. History tells us that when scientists willingly endorse sweeping governmental agendas fueled by dodgy science, bad things soon happen. To borrow the meter of Winston Churchill, never in the history of pseudoscientific consensus will so much be done to so many by so few.[2]

As successive National Climate Assessments have been published, forecasts for future U.S. climate have become more specific and detailed. For example, there is this from the third assessment, "However, if emissions of heat-trapping gases continue their upward trend, clear patterns of precipitation change are projected to emerge."

Such a statement is known as a forecast. Forecasts have discrete timelines because they are about what is going to happen in the future. One may be for tomorrow's temperature, another for next winter's, or maybe one for changes in precipitation generated by global warming over the next 100 years. So, when the USGCRP says, "clear patterns of precipitation change are projected to emerge," there

[2] The referenced massive regulatory intrusion is our characterization of "President Obama's Climate Action Plan."

must be both a location and a timeframe. The 2014 report maps out changes in precipitation forecast between the 1961–79 averaging period and 2080–99.

Nowhere in the assessment is the concept of forecast utility discussed. This concept, which best translates as "usefulness," clearly depends upon how far into the future the prospective changes are forecast to appear.

The 2014 assessment highlights areas in which its 15 climate models are largely in agreement as to the direction (above or below normal) of forecast precipitation changes—but it does not say when those changes will emerge from the background noise. If it will take an extremely long time to detect such a change, why would any forecast change matter?

We examined the regions where "high-confidence" predictions were made. We first determined the percent changes in seasonal rainfall that the USGCRP predicted and compared them with the observed variability of year-to-year precipitation, as measured by the standard deviation.[3]

We then calculated the standard deviation (in percentage of the mean) around the observed (1901–2011) precipitation data for each high-confidence state. Dividing the observed standard deviation by the projected change per year provided us the time (in years) until the projected change exceeds one standard deviation of observed variability in a given state.

There were 84 separate season-state combinations in which confidence is "high." In nine, the predicted change already has emerged from the noise, some 80 years ahead of the 2080–99 forecast target. We're not certain if this is good or bad for the models. Of the nine, eight are precipitation increases, with most of them in springtime, so farmers should be doing handstands.

There were 75 remaining cases in which the observed change to date is less than the model-projected change. During the summer, the average time for the projected changes to emerge from the natural noise (thereby exceeding 1 standard deviation) is 520 years! In wintertime, it's 330 years. Averaged across all seasons, it will take

---

[3] One standard deviation encompasses roughly two-thirds of the data of a normally distributed variable. So one-sixth of the observations are higher or lower than one standard deviation.

Figure 27

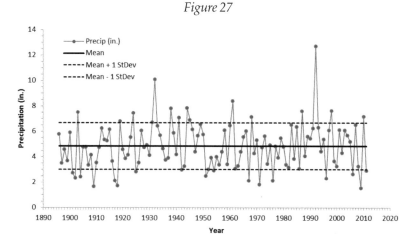

Note: Figures in the third National Climate Assessment indicate that declining winter precipitation in Texas will be statistically detectable (meaning that it will average one standard deviation below the current average) over 1,200 years from now. The average time for any change to be detectable is around 300 years, thanks to the great natural year-to-year variability in precipitation data.[4]

approximately 297 years before a state's seasonal-projected precipitation change emerges from background variability—and this is only for those states and seasons in which the USGCRP says the forecast is high confidence. For most of the rest of the country, the time for emergence from the statistical noise is longer still. An example is shown in Figure 27.

The fact that it generally takes so long to observe any change in forecast precipitation means the forecasts have very little utility. Ask yourself how much you would be willing to risk on a questionable forecast of a change in rainfall that can't be detected for another 300 years.

If that seems hard to believe, Table 2 provides the results from a few selected states and season combinations. Where we have "n/a," that means no high-confidence forecast was made. Where the text

[4] Data from National Centers for Environmental Information, National Oceanic and Atmospheric Administration, http://www.ncdc.noaa.gov/cag. Analysis by the authors.

State	Winter	Spring	Summer	Fall
		Table 2		
AZ	**1,102**	**221**	n/a	n/a
CA	n/a	**332**	**2,111**	467
NY	112	120	n/a	n/a
TX	**1,217**	**206**	n/a	n/a
VA	*319*	n/a	n/a	n/a

is in bold face, there's a forecast decrease. Where it's in roman, there's to be an increase.

Lukewarmers are concerned when governments issue climate change forecasts called "clear patterns of precipitation change" without discussing their utility.

22. Paris: December 10, 2015

> Chuck Todd, host of *Meet the Press*: There seems to be no mechanism for getting countries to comply other than wagging your finger at them and shaming them.
>
> Secretary of State John Kerry: [That's] the most powerful weapon in many ways.

Nothing much happened during the Paris conference over the weekend of December 5–6, 2015. Weather claimed center stage in Scotland where record or near-record flooding was brought on by Storm Desmond. The *Guardian's* George Monbiot wasted no time in blaming the storm on global warming. But, by late in the conference's second week, plenty more started to happen in Paris.[1]

A curious disconnection from reality began to infiltrate drafts of a proposed agreement. Todd Stern, the chief U.S. negotiator, aligned himself with the mostly small, poor, and tropical nations calling for the agreement to limit post-Industrial Revolution warming to 1.5°C instead of 2.0°C. Might this be interpreted as an admission that the UN climate models are wrong? As noted earlier, the mean sensitivity of the UN's climate models—or overall warming projected for a doubling of the concentration of carbon dioxide in the atmosphere—is 3.2°C (5.8°F).

Based upon calculations made by Gerald Meehl, of the National Center for Atmospheric Research, in Boulder, Colorado, these models have 0.6°C (1.1°F) of unrealized warming built into them at today's concentrations. We have already experienced nearly 0.9°C (1.6°F), and the Paris documents indicated (erroneously) that all global warming has been caused by greenhouse gas emissions. So, if Stern and his allies are serious, then *all global emissions must go to zero immediately.*

---

[1] George Monbiot, "Do Little, Hide the Evidence: the Official Neglect that Caused These Deadly Floods," *Guardian* (London), December 7, 2015, http://www.theguardian.com/commentisfree/2015/dec/07/hide-evidence-storm-desmond-floods-paris-talks.

Given that everyone knows this to be impossible, the only way it could be achieved is if the true sensitivity is lower than the mean in the UN models. In other words, what the United States sought only is possible in a lukewarming world. It is also scientific nonsense.

It is clear that a substantial portion of the observed temperature rise necessarily was caused by factors other than carbon dioxide. The rise largely is accomplished within two statistically equal periods of warming, one from roughly 1910 to 1945 and the other from 1976 to 1998. If the first was brought on by carbon dioxide emissions, the temperature sensitivity has to be enormous because there were relatively few emissions of carbon dioxide before and during that period. Even so, the evidence is that the sensitivity is lukewarm.

Meanwhile, U.S. negotiators, having already pledged $3 billion per year to the so-called Green Climate Fund by 2020, said the United States also would double its commitment for adaptation to climate change in developing nations from $430 million to $860 million per year. What isn't clear is from where this money is supposed to come. The president can't commit money that Congress hasn't appropriated and the Constitution clearly stipulates that all appropriations must originate in the House of Representatives, a legislative body that appears to be gerrymandered to sustain a Republican majority until at least January 2023, after the first congressional election based upon 2020 census data.[2]

By 2020, the developed world's contributions to the Green Climate Fund are supposed to total $100 billion per year. Obviously, a figmented U.S. $3 billion contribution won't represent much of a drop in that very large bucket.

Coincidentally, the Organization for Economic Cooperation and Development (OECD) claims that after counting public monies, grants-in-kind, charity, loans, and just about every other dollar going from the OECD to the developing world as climate-related, $62 billion per year already has been committed by 2020. This wasn't well received by the putative recipients. Brazil, South Africa, and India objected to including loans and the double-counting of already-committed foreign aid. China's climate negotiator Xie Zhenhua agreed, saying, "We do not recognize the [OECD] numbers."

---

[2] That is, barring a Donald Trump-induced 2016 electoral catastrophe.

A revised draft agreement appeared by the end of the day stating that the goal of the agreement would be to "hold the increase in global average temperature to well below 2°C above pre-industrial levels and to pursue efforts to limit the increase to 1.5°C." It is doubtful the negotiators appreciated that achieving that goal would mean the world would immediately have to cut its carbon dioxide emissions to zero.

23. U.S. Temperature Assessments: Cherries for the Picking

I warn you against believing that advertising is a science.

—William Bernbach*

Lukewarmers become very queasy when governments cherry-pick data in their climate policy compendia in the service of alarmism. The most recent National Climate Assessment does a wonderful job of this when it comes to the U.S. temperature history and claims in the first chapter that more than 80 percent of the observed warming in this country has taken place since 1980, to wit, "U.S average temperature has increased by about 1.5 deg. F since 1895; more than 80% of this increase has occurred since 1980."

Take a look at the National Climatic Data Center's own records ending in 2012, the last year of data in the assessment (Figure 28).[1]

The 80 percent figure is a consequence of massive cherry picking. The U.S. lower-48-state temperature history is a series of ups and downs more correctly characterized as (1) no change from the beginning of the record from 1895 to 1910, (2) a rise of about 0.9°C (1.6°F) from 1910 to 1940, (3) a fall of about 0.4°C (0.7°F) from 1940 to 1980, and (4) a rise of 1.0°C (1.8°F) from 1980 to 2012.

---

* William Bernbach (1911–82) was an advertising creative director and a founder of the international advertising agency Doyle Dane Bernbach—literally one of the "Mad Men" upon whom characters in the AMC series were modeled.

[1] We recognize that more than half of the warming in this record is due to adjustments and "homogenization" of data. However, no systematic refutation of the adjustment methodology has been forthcoming to date. Ross McKitrick and Terence Kealey of Cato Institute's Center for the Study of Science have assembled a high-powered team of climate scientists and statisticians who will be taking another look. But for now, we are stuck with the record that we show here.

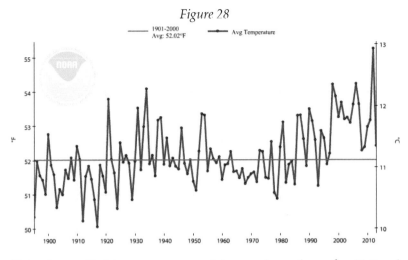

Figure 28

Note: Lower-48-state average annual temperatures from the National Climatic Data Center.[2]

Alternatively, the assessment simply could have taken the overall rate of temperature rise (0.13°F, or 0.07°C, per decade), multiplied it by the number of decades since 1980 (3.3), and divided the result by the overall temperature change of 1.5°F (0.8°C). The result from that calculation reveals that 29 percent of the overall rise occurred since 1980—nowhere near the more than 80 percent claimed.

Yet another approach would be to determine the maximum amount of temperature rise that occurred at any time before 1980 and then determine how much more than that the temperature has risen. For example, from 1895 to 1940, lower-48-state temperature increased at a rate of 0.15°C (0.27°F) per decade for 4.5 decades, thereby yielding a total rise of 0.7°C (1.2°F). That only leaves 0.2°C (0.3°F) of the total rise left over and makes the maximum proportion of the temperature rise since 1980 around 20 percent. That figure certainly doesn't seem to be a "key deliverable for President Obama's Climate Action Plan."

Here's how one can get close to the assessment's 80 percent figure: calculate the linear temperature rise between 1895 and 1979, subtract that from the total (1895–2012), and assign whatever is left over to the period 1980–2012. That calculation would seemingly show 77 percent of the rise occurred since 1980, which rounds to 80.

Finally, you could decide to calculate the linear rise from 1980 to 2012 and compare it with the total rise. The rise that results from 1980 to 2012 is 0.9°C, or 105 percent of the total. Call the president; start the presses; a key deliverable is ready!

We must hasten to point out that none of these methods is statistically sound due to the obviously nonlinear changes in temperature that characterize the lower-48-state temperature record. What this does illustrate is that there is a wide variety of answers available depending upon what number you wish to get. The assessment's authors clearly chose a method that would produce a lot of rise since 1980 while disregarding the fact that a totally similar rise took place between 1910 and 1940, a time before greenhouse gas changes possibly could have had much influence on temperature. That's the cherry that was picked.

Traditionally, U.S. temperature records concern temperatures in what are referred to as the lower 48 states, where the history very much resembles that of global surface land temperature, albeit with less warming. But including Alaska, which contains 17.5 percent of the total U.S. land area, makes for a far different story.[3] The Alaska temperature history is shown in Figure 29.

Here's what the 2014 assessment says about the "Last Frontier":

> Over the past 60 years, Alaska has warmed more than twice as rapidly as the rest of the United States, with statewide average annual air temperature increasing by 3°F and average winter temperature by 6°F, with substantial year-to-year and regional variability. Most of the warming occurred around 1976 during a shift in a long-lived climate pattern (the Pacific Decadal Oscillation [PDO]) from a cooler pattern to a warmer one. The PDO has been shown to alternate over time between warm and cool phases. The underlying long-term warming trend has moderated the effects of the more recent shift of the PDO to its cooler phase in the early 2000s.

---

[3] This clearly is a misnomer that relates only to Alaska. Hawaii is considerably farther south than the legacy 48 states. The latitude at Key West, Florida, is 24.6°N, while Hilo, Hawaii, is 19.7°N. That makes Hawaii "lower."

Figure 29

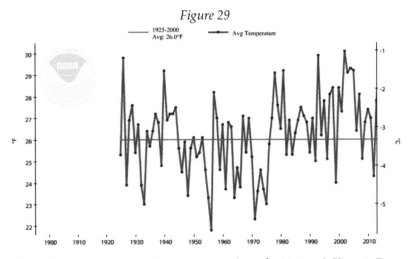

Note: Alaska average annual temperatures from the National Climatic Data Center, 1925–2012.[4]

Appreciating that temperatures reported in the 2014 assessment run through 2012, we note that the 60 years would span 1953–2012. And, as reported, the rise during that period is very close to 3°F (1.7°C). But what a convenient year to start! It is very close to the mid-1950s low point in Alaska's available temperature record. Why ignore the data from 1925 to the early 1950s to focus on the past 60 years? Well, doing that would cut the warming trend in half, a pretty sour cherry to pick.

The authors of the assessment are right to note that there was a climate shift in 1976. It's more colloquially known as the "Great Pacific Climate Shift" and shows up very clearly in the Alaskan data compiled by the Arctic Climate Research Center at the University of Alaska–Fairbanks (Figure 30). Observant readers will note that data from the National Climatic Data Center (NCDC) generally are warmer in recent years than are the data from the University of Alaska. For example, 2012 is about 2°F below the long-term average reflected in the university data while the NCDC data shows it to be a degree warmer. This is in large part because the University of Alaska

---

[4] Data from National Centers for Environmental Information, National Oceanic and Atmospheric Administration, http://www.ncdc.noaa.gov/cag/.

doesn't "homogenize" data. Homogenization is a pretty dodgy procedure given how sparse the data are to begin with.[5]

Figure 30

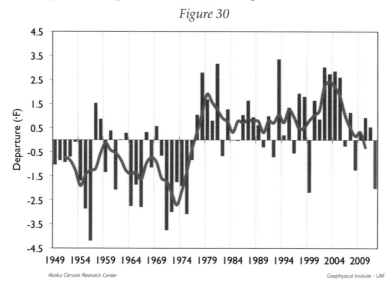

Alaska Climate Research Center   Geophysical Institute - UAF

Note: Mean annual temperature departure data from the Alaska Climate Research Center graphically show that climate change in Alaska comes down to a single shift that occurred in the mid-1970s, known as the "Great Pacific Climate Shift."[6]

99

---

[5] Homogenization is an attempt to reconcile data from *nearby* weather stations. In Alaska, there are very few nearby stations. The NCDC algorithm clearly searches for the "nearest" ones, even if they aren't nearby!

[6] Arthur J. Miller et al., "The 1976–77 Climate Shift of the Pacific Ocean," *Oceanography* 7 (1994): 21–26. Data from Alaska Climate Research Center, http://climate .gi.alaska.edu/ClimTrends/Change/TempChange.html.

24. Alternative Reality: The Lukewarmer's Greener World

> Did you know that the Earth is getting greener, quite literally? Satellites are now confirming that the amount of green vegetation on the planet has been increasing for three decades. This will be news to those accustomed to alarming tales about deforestation, overdevelopment and ecosystem destruction.
>
> —Matt Ridley*

Despite obvious federal government pressure to produce end-of-the-world science, the legacies of Sylvan Wittwer and Paul Waggoner largely have spared the fields of plant ecology and agronomy from the global warming madness. Their findings, which include pioneering work on the fertilization effects of carbon dioxide, are being verified daily in the real world.

Photosynthesis—or the fixing of CO_2 in the form of plant carbohydrates—is a complex series of biochemical equations. Increasing the atmosphere's CO_2 concentration results in more plant material, as well as higher production per increment of water. Plants grown in an environment with higher CO_2 become more efficient in their use of water due to a decline in the number of stomates (pores in plant leaves) through which water can escape. This makes sense from an evolutionary standpoint, as most plants we see around us today originally evolved on a warmer planet with a higher atmospheric CO_2 concentration than there is today. How big is the CO_2 fertilization effect? Cato Institute scholar Craig Idso writes:

> At the fundamental level, carbon dioxide is the basis of nearly all life on Earth, as it is the primary raw material or "food"

---

* Matthew White Ridley is a British journalist, author of several terrific books about science, and a member of the House of Lords. He is quoted from the *Wall Street Journal*, January 5, 2013.

Figure 31

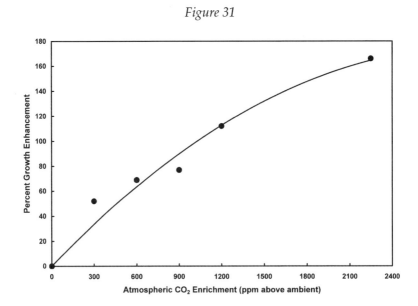

Note: Percent growth enhancement as a function of atmospheric CO_2 enrichment in parts per million (ppm) above the normal or ambient atmospheric CO_2 concentration, showing that the growth benefits continue to accrue well beyond an atmospheric CO_2 concentration of 2,000 ppm. These data, representing a wide mix of plant species, were derived from 1,087 individual experiments described in 342 peer-reviewed scientific journal articles written by 484 scientists residing in 28 countries and representing 142 different research institutions.[1]

that is utilized by plants to produce the organic matter out of which they construct their tissues.

Typically, a doubling of the air's CO_2 content above present-day concentrations raises the productivity of most herbaceous plants by about one-third; this positive response occurs in plants that utilize all three of the major biochemical pathways of photosynthesis.[2]

[1] Patrick J. Michaels, ed., *ADDENDUM*, p. 104.

[2] Ibid., pp. 103–4.

Figure 32

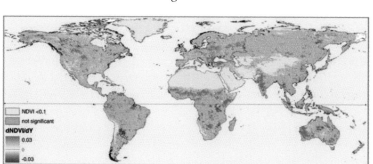

Note: Spatial trends in net primary plant productivity, 1981–2006.[3]

Agricultural plants shouldn't be the sole beneficiaries of the salutary effects of CO_2. It is difficult to isolate CO_2's influence due to increasing genetic improvement, better agronomic practices like "no-till" agriculture, and the insertion of novel DNA into the genomes (AKA "genetic engineering"). Clearly, the "fertilization" effect of CO_2 produces a "difficult prediction," namely that the planet literally should be getting greener as CO_2 rises.

In 1997, Ranga Myneni and his colleagues from Boston University published the first satellite data showing a systematic greening of large portions of the planet. The satellite data were transformed into the "Normalized Difference Vegetation Index," or NDVI. Since then, this original work has been expanded and has yielded some remarkable results.[4,5]

Note that there are three areas of truly remarkable semidesert greening: the western portion of monsoonal India, sub-Saharan (Sahelian) Africa, and arid southwestern Australia. Entering a Google search for "deserts expanding global warming" will yield about 800,000 hits, but what is seen in Figure 32 and in reality is the opposite—the earth is getting greener.

---

[3] Rogier de Jong et al., "Analysis of Monotonic Greening and Browning Trends from Global NDVI Time-Series," *Remote Sensing of Environment* 115 (2011): 692–702.

[4] Ibid.

[5] R. B. Myneni et al., "Increased Plant Growth in the Northern High Latitudes from 1981 to 1991," *Nature* 386 (1997): 698–702.

Additionally, mid-latitude North America and Europe—especially west of the Volga River—also show substantial greening, likely a result of an observed lengthening of the growing season (the time between the last frost in the spring and the first frost in fall) in addition to CO_2 fertilization. There's also an intriguing (albeit thin) strip of sharp greening at the northernmost margin of the vegetated region of North America, a sign of salubrious change in the formerly barren subarctic.

Lukewarmers note that the primary effects of greenhouse warming and increased atmospheric CO_2 are a slight warming on a greener planet.

25. Back to the Genetic Garden of Eden?

> [By] 1995, the greenhouse effect would be desolating the heartlands of North America and Eurasia with horrific drought, causing crop failures and food riots. . . . [By 1996] the Platte River of Nebraska would be dry, while a continent-wide black blizzard of prairie topsoil will stop traffic on interstates, strip paint from houses and shut down computers. . . . The Mexican police will round up illegal American migrants surging into Mexico seeking work as field hands.
>
> —Michael Oppenheimer*

A large amount of what we directly and indirectly consume is produced by flowering plants known as angiosperms. Angiosperms began their explosive spread throughout the biosphere 100 million years ago in what is called the mid-Cretaceous period. That was one of the hottest periods in the evolutionary record (though not as warm as the Paleocene–Eocene Thermal Maximum). It was a time of very active volcanic activity that drove carbon dioxide concentrations to about 600 percent of preindustrial values. By way of comparison, by 2015 the concentration has risen to about 43 percent above the preindustrial concentration.

If one looks at it through the prism of geologic time, Earth's atmosphere is pretty impoverished in terms of its CO_2 concentration when compared with most of the past 100 million years. It's also important to note that the atmospheric concentration of CO_2 during the height of the recent ice ages was almost too low to support plant life at all. So what can we expect to happen if CO_2 gradually transitions away from the concentration of around 300 parts per million characteristic of interglacial periods and continues to grow to higher levels?

---

* Michael Oppenheimer is a climate scientist and Albert G. Milbank Professor of Geosciences and International Affairs in the Woodrow Wilson School of Public and International Affairs at Princeton University. The quotation is from *Dead Heat: The Race against the Greenhouse Effect*, his 1990 book with Robert H. Boyle about the effects of carbon dioxide on climate (Melksham, U.K.: Redwood Press, 1990). It's not a novel.

Figure 33

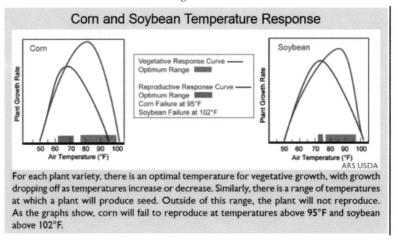

Note: Illustration and caption from page 27 of the USGCRP's report *Global Climate Change Impacts in the United States*, also known as the second National Climate Assessment.[1]

The U.S. Global Change Research Program's (USGCRP) 2009 assessment (see Figure 33) paints a pretty chilling image accompanied by some alarming text.

The purple curves are plant growth rates during the reproductive (flowering) stages of corn and soybeans. Note that the optimum temperature is a daily average of around 65°F for corn and around 70°F for soybeans (which is why soybean production is favored over corn in the steamy Mississippi Delta). Like young *Homo sapiens*, plants are much more vulnerable in their reproductive phases than in their vegetative ones (green curves).

But there's a critical thing missing from this apparent horror show: if summer temperatures are driven upward by increasing atmospheric CO_2, flowering plants are pretty much going back to their Cretaceous roots. Do they genetically possess a mechanism to grow better under higher temperatures if the CO_2 concentration is driven upward? Or to put it another way, have angiosperms such as corn and soybeans lost their ability to thrive under Cretaceous-like

---

[1] Karl et al., *Global Climate Change Impacts*, p. 27.

conditions? A remarkable paper published over 30 years ago in *Plant Physiology* demonstrates they have not.[2]

What we have learned from this and other studies is that as CO_2 increases, the temperature optimum for growth also rises. At 10°C (50°F) plants (in this case, bigtooth aspen) show no response to elevated CO_2. But as the temperature continues to rise, higher concentrations begin to dramatically increase growth rates. For this particular species, under mid-20th century concentrations of around 325 ppm, the optimum leaf temperature for growth is around 25°C (77°F). Under more Cretaceous-like conditions in which concentrations are a bit below 2,000 ppm, the optimum temperature rises to 36°C (97°F). Further, the hot limit (the point at which plants consume more carbohydrates than they produce) also rises by 11°C.

Note also the remarkable change in growth rate that occurs in a hotter atmosphere under conditions of enhanced CO_2. As shown in our graph in Figure 34, the maximum photosynthetic rate—the rate at which these plants form green matter—increases over threefold under Cretaceous-like conditions. For a more technical view, we have inserted a copy of page 103 of Cato Institute's *ADDENDUM: Global Climate Change Impacts in the United States.*[3]

What is most remarkable is that increasing concentrations of CO_2 raise the temperature limit for photosynthetic life. It long has been known that the enzymes that promote respiration in cold-blooded animals change their shape as temperature rises—for example, allowing fish to thrive in warmer waters than are found in their home ranges. The same may apply to plants.[4]

[2] Thomas W. Jurik et al., "Short-Term Effect of CO_2 on Gas Exchange of Leaves of Bigtooth Aspen (*Populus grandidentata*) in the Field," *Plant Physiology* 75 (1984): 1022–26.

[3] Keith E. Idso and Sherwood B. Idso, "Plant Responses to Atmospheric CO_2 Enrichment in the Face of Environmental Constraints: A Review of the Past 10 Years' Research," *Agricultural and Forest Meteorology* 69 (1994): 153–203. The notation in the illustration Figure 34 that net photosynthesis becomes negative at 50°C is an extrapolation of the y-axis in the accompanying graph.

[4] Peter W. Hochachka and George N. Somero, *Biochemical Adaption: Mechanism and Process in Physiological Evolution* (New York: Oxford University Press, 2002).

Figure 34

The CO₂-Temperature-Growth Interaction

The growth-enhancing effects of elevated CO_2 typically increase with rising temperature. This phenomenon is noted in experiments that exposed bigtooth aspen leaves to atmospheric CO_2 concentrations of 325 and 1935 ppm and measured their photosynthetic rates at a number of different temperatures. The figure below reproduces their results and slightly extends the two relationships defined by their data to both warmer and cooler conditions.

At 10°C, elevated CO_2 has essentially no effect on net photosynthesis in this particular species, as has been demonstrated is characteristic of plants in general. At 25°C, however, where the net photosynthetic rate of the leaves exposed to 325 ppm CO_2 is maximal, the extra CO_2 of this study boosts the net photosynthetic rate of the foliage by nearly 100%; and at 36°C, where the net photosynthetic rate of the leaves exposed to 1935 ppm CO_2 is maximal, the extra CO_2 boosts the net photosynthetic rate of the foliage by a whopping 450%. In addition, it is readily seen that the extra CO_2 increases the optimum temperature for net photosynthesis in this species by about 11°C: from 25°C in air of 325 ppm CO_2 to 36°C in air of 1935 ppm CO_2.

In viewing the warm-temperature projections of the two relationships, it can also be seen that the transition from positive to negative net photosynthesis - which denotes a change from life-sustaining to life-depleting conditions - likely occurs somewhere in the vicinity of 39°C in air of 325 ppm CO_2 but somewhere in the vicinity of 50°C in air of 1935 ppm CO_2. Hence, not only was the optimum temperature for the growth of bigtooth aspen greatly increased by the extra CO_2 of this experiment, so too was the temperature above which life cannot be sustained increased, and by about the same amount, i.e., 11°C.

References

Idso, K.E. and Idso, S.B. 1994. Plant responses to atmospheric CO_2 enrichment in the face of environmental constraints: A review of the past 10 years' research. *Agricultural and Forest Meteorology* **69**: 153-203.

Jurik, T.W., Weber, J.A. and Gates, D.M. 1984. Short-term effects of CO_2 on gas exchange of leaves of bigtooth aspen (*Populus grandidentata*) in the field. *Plant Physiology* **75**: 1022-1026.

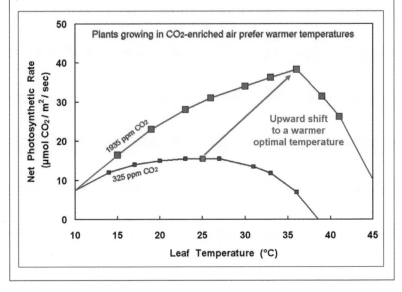

Note: Illustration and accompanying text from page 103 of the 2012 Cato Institute *ADDENDUM: Global Climate Change Impacts in the United States.*[5]

---

[5] Michaels, ed., *ADDENDUM*, p. 103.

Lukewarmers note that life has thrived on Earth through hot times and cold, mostly with much higher CO_2 concentrations and warmer temperatures than we are experiencing in the current era. We'll say it again: enhanced CO_2 allows plants to take advantage of warmer temperatures.

26. Rational Optimism in the Lukewarm World[1]

The battle to feed humanity is over. In the 1970s, the world will undergo famines. Hundreds of millions of people are going to starve to death in spite of any crash programs embarked upon now.

—Paul Ehrlich*

Life expectancy has more than doubled in the developed world since 1900. Per capita wealth has increased approximately 11-fold. Healthy, wealthy, and diversified societies are only marginally sensitive to weather and climate. Consider agriculture, perhaps the most weather-sensitive, large-scale activity on Earth. Historical corn yields in the United States (the world's largest producer) are shown in Figure 35.

Forty years ago, President Obama's science adviser John Holdren, Paul Ehrlich, and the fashionable limits-to-growth crowd were completely convinced crop yields had attained their maximum and that worldwide famine was just around the corner. It would be brought about by pollution and climate change. As we realize now, that simply didn't come to pass. (Ehrlich would add, kind of like people who can't let go of a forecast blizzard, "not yet.") When he wrote *The Population Bomb*, Ehrlich was concerned about the prospect of global cooling.

---

* Paul R. Ehrlich is an American ecologist and demographer. He is Bing Professor of Population Studies in the biological sciences department at Stanford University. This statement kicked off the first edition of what may be his best-known work, *The Population Bomb* (New York: Ballantine Books, 1968).

[1] We've borrowed this term from Matt Ridley, author of *The Rational Optimist: How Prosperity Evolves* (New York: HarperCollins, 2001) and "Matt Ridley: My Life as a Climate Change Lukewarmer," *Times* (London), January 19, 2015, http://www.thetimes.co.uk/tto/life/article4325798.ece.

Figure 35

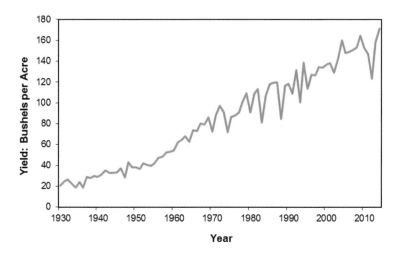

Note: U.S. corn yields, 1930–2013.[2]

This consistent yield increase got under way in the 1930s and largely was due to Henry Wallace's commercialization of hybrid corn.[3] The Haber-Bosch process for fixing atmospheric nitrogen in the form of portable anhydrous ammonia provided cheap and abundant fertilizer (especially after World War II) and greatly raised yields. Genetic and mechanical improvements, more efficient tillage methods, and market forces have worked together to continually drive yield upward (see Figure 35). There is no end in sight.

It is generally assumed that all the factors raising crop yields sum up to a linear (constant) rate of increase. Deviations from this technology-induced trend are attributed to unusually good or bad

---

[2] Data from National Agricultural Statistics Service, http://www.nass.usda.gov.

[3] Henry Wallace (1888–1965) is perhaps best known as the Progressive Party candidate for president in 1948. He previously served alongside Franklin D. Roosevelt as 33rd vice president of the United States (1941–45). He was Roosevelt's secretary of agriculture (1933–40) and secretary of commerce (1945–46). But wait, there's more! Wallace was a pioneering statistician who developed crop yield models and published sophisticated statistical studies. In 1926, he used a part of his wife's small inheritance to found Hi-Bred Corn Company. It survives to this day as Pioneer Hi-Bred, a subsidiary of DuPont Corporation. A life in full.

weather or, in some cases, disease outbreaks such as the 1969–70 southern corn leaf blight.

Figure 36 shows that the largest negative departures from the trend are on the order of a mere 10 percent of the crop. The massive secular increase in yields in the past 85 years, therefore, insulates us from famine. In the worst year in recent memory (2012), national yields still were twice what they had been in 1960—and *five times* what they were in the 1930s. Similar behavior is seen among all major crops.

It is clear that people in the developed world are living longer, healthier lives in a warming climate. Most of the world's civilizations have developed under a wide range of climates. Humans live comfortably in seasonal daily temperatures varying from −40°F upward to 115°F. People who live in the United States are particularly adapted to a very broad range of climates—from the extreme cold of central Alaska to teeming desert cities like Las Vegas and Phoenix, where temperatures can reach 110°F (43°C), and on to the tropical climate of southeastern Florida.

Poorer countries' vulnerability to climate change largely is a function of their inability to access global markets. No location on Earth experiences salutary weather and climate all the time. Nations that are not agriculturally productive purchase from those that are. Those living in variable environments alternatively export and import food. Since the advent of modern technological agriculture, there never has been a systematic and worldwide food shortage brought on by weather and climate. In fact, it's the diversity and variability of climate that ensures our interwoven security. Economic and technological development—largely powered by fossil fuels—has enabled the weather sensitivity of global agriculture to drop monotonically.

What began in the United States has spread around the world, except into very poor countries.[4]

But it's not just corn. It's pretty much all of the major crops.

---

[4] The labor efficiency of the American agricultural model is truly breathtaking. In 1800, about 85 percent of the nation's working population was engaged in agriculture. That dropped to 41 percent by 1900 and to 16 percent by 1945. Today, 1.5 percent of Americans are actively engaged in agriculture. (Source: "The 20th Century Transformation of U.S. Agriculture and Farm Policy," U.S. Department of Agriculture–Economic Research Service economic information bulletin no. 3, June 2005.)

Figure 36

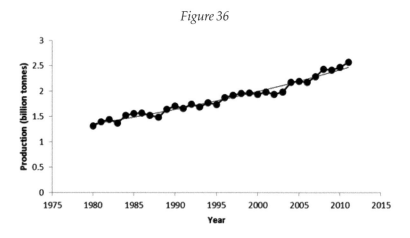

Note: Global annual production from maize (corn), rice, soybeans, and wheat.[5]

An upward-rising curve, shown in Figure 36, representing a low-order exponential increase explains 97 percent of the interannual variation in production. We know of no study in the refereed or gray literature (or even in blogoworld) that says there's an improvement in worldwide growing conditions that is getting exponentially better. Rather, what appears to be taking place is an exponential increase in production brought about through a combination of technological improvements and efficiency in the use of arable land, as well as the increase in atmospheric carbon dioxide.[6]

Why is the behavior of the global food system so smooth and monotonic, as the graph shows? The truth is, no one really knows. But whatever the incentive to which individual growers respond (making money, for one), their uncommunicated, communal behavior—thanks to some invisible hand—changes so little from year to year that a simple parabolic equation explains an enormous amount of the year-to-year variation we experience.

People who model crop yield and production usually assume the deviations from a smooth trend are due to weather. But because of

---

[5] Food and Agriculture Organization of the United Nations statistics at http://faostat3.fao.org/home/E.

[6] Predicted production 52,283.3 – 2.32 (year) + 0.00059 (year^2).

the vastly different climatic regions in which the world's crops are grown, it's apparent that bad weather in one place tends to be canceled out by better conditions elsewhere. Otherwise the deviations from the smooth trend would be large and obvious.

Using these assumptions, the biggest dent in global crop production was in 2002—a reduction of 6.3 percent below the trendline. For what it's worth, the last four years of this record are all positive, averaging right around 2.0 percent above the trendline.

Lukewarmers know that economic development is the key in adaptation to the vagaries of weather and climate, even climatic change induced by people.

27. Food to Burn

> Despite attempts of containment, such as the Calvinistic doctrine of predestination, extended witch-hunts took place at the various peaks of the Little Ice Age because a part of society held the witches directly responsible for the high frequency of climatic anomalies and the impacts thereof. The enormous tensions created in society as a result of the persecution of witches demonstrate how dangerous it is to discuss climatic change under the aspects of morality.
>
> —Wolfgang Behringer[*]

In 2011, Stanford University's David Lobell and various colleagues reported in *Science* that human-caused global warming from 1980–2008 had reduced global crop yield, defined as the amount produced per acre. Modeling the climate response of the world's four largest commodity crops (corn, rice, wheat, and soybeans), Lobell's team calculated that as a result of rising temperatures and precipitation changes, global crop yield was about 3 percent less than it otherwise would have been.[1, 2]

---

[*] Wolfgang Behringer is a German historian specializing in witchcraft beliefs of early modern Europe. The quotation is from "Climatic Change and Witch-Hunting: The Impact of the Little Ice Age on Mentalities," in *Climate Variability in Sixteenth Century Europe and Its Social Dimension*, ed. Christian Pfister, Rudolf Brázdil, and Rüdiger Glaser (The Netherlands: Springer, 1999) and reprinted in *Climatic Change* 43 (1999).

[1] David B. Lobell et al., "Climate Trends and Global Crop Production since 1980," *Science* 333 (2011): 616–20.

[2] The title of Lobell's paper is misleading. It actually concerns crop *yield*, which is the quantity per planted or harvested acre. "Production" is the amount harvested and is the product of yield multiplied by acreage. Had the authors actually modeled production, they would have pretty much killed the weather issue—as should be obvious from our Figure 36 (Chapter 26), where the presumably weather-related deviations from the trend line are generally very small, and the trend itself is very robust.

Does this mean anything? What it amounts to is a drop in a huge vat of ethanol. Consider this: the United States produces about 36 percent of the world's corn, approximately half of which is used to manufacture ethanol as a gasoline substitute in an attempt to lower net CO_2 emissions from driving and to restrain climate change. Corn makes up 30 percent of total worldwide production of the four crops studied by Lobell's group.[3, 4]

Multiplying all those percentages reveals that the United States is burning a bit more than 4 percent of total global main crop production in an attempt to mitigate a purportedly climate-driven loss of 3 percent in global crop production. Looked at that way, this policy is about as crazy as burning witches because of climate change and associated crop failures during the Little Ice Age.

Because of the availability cascade, we were unable to find a single news story among the many published concerning Lobell's paper that noted how crop productivity doubled during the study period. The study's entire premise is hypothetical and based upon global crop yields the authors would have predicted had there been no climate change whatsoever, versus what actually was observed. To make matters worse, their 3 percent drop in crop yield would be less than 1 percent if they had factored in the direct fertilization effect of increasing atmospheric CO_2. The authors are honest enough to note that their result might be "overly pessimistic" because they fail to incorporate the effects of long-term adaptive farming responses to changing climates (as if a 1 percent decline in the face of a 100 percent increase has any meaning whatsoever). Farmers are not as dumb as statistical models make them out to be.[5]

What all this means is that the United States annually burns more than four times as much grain as climate change could possibly take

---

[3] Agronomists routinely refer to the United States as "the Saudi Arabia of corn." With the recent boom in domestic oil production, perhaps this should now be rephrased "the North Dakota of corn."

[4] It doesn't. See Timothy Searchinger et al., "Use of U.S. Croplands for Biofuels Increases Greenhouse Gases through Emissions from Land-Use Change," *Science* 319 (2008): 1238–40.

[5] We took it upon ourselves to incorporate the effects of long-term adaptive farming in crafting our production graph. If climate were becoming increasingly bad— and producers and the agrosystem weren't adapting—the negative departures from the trend line would be increasing. They aren't.

away, if climate change were to take away anything at all. Thinking about this in terms of the future, were we to experience twice as much climate change from 2010 to 2038 as we did from 1980 to 2008 (the period Lobell's team studied), the rational policy response would be to stop burning half of the corn for ethanol that we now do. We'd make up for the entire reduction in global climate-related crop production.

The irrational fear that climate change will lead to global crop failures is risible; climate simply is too diverse and agriculture too dispersed. Burning crops in the form of ethanol to alleviate that fear ultimately condemns the perpetrators of such policies to the status of permanent laughingstocks alongside those who fanned the flames under witches, warlocks—and lukewarmers.[6]

Lukewarmers know that market forces compel adaptation to all kinds of change, including slight changes in climate. They also recognize that even if the United States continues to burn half its corn production, the rest of the world still is able to produce tremendous amounts of food to meet the needs of its growing population.

---

[6] On May 29, 2015, Sen. Sheldon Whitehouse (D-RI) took to the *Washington Post*'s op-ed pages to propose prosecuting those in the "climate denial network" using federal RICO-racketeering standards. Lukewarmers, according to his analysis, this includes you.

28. Is Global Warming Making Us Ill?

> Climate change related obsessions and/or compulsions were identified in 28 percent of patients presenting with obsessive-compulsive disorder. Their obsessions included leaving taps on and wasting water, leaving lights on and wasting electricity, pets dying of thirst, leaving the stove on and wasting gas as well as obsessions that global warming had contributed to house floors cracking, pipes leaking, roof problems, and white ants eating the house.
>
> —Royal Australian and New Zealand Congress of Psychiatrists (2010)

As the relentless propaganda for the December 2015 UN-sponsored Parisian climate convocation spilled forth, the Obama administration proclaimed on April 7, 2015, a new initiative to address the health effects of climate change. And (coincidence of coincidences) the U.S. Global Change Research Program (USGCRP) announced on the same day that it had produced a draft report titled "The Impacts of Climate Change on Human Health in the United States: A Scientific Assessment."

The report does not accept the totality of science on human health and climate. It instead preferred to put forward alarming narratives, many of them more based upon science fiction. In this way, it is similar to previous USGCRP reports, in particular the human health chapter in the 2014 National Climate Assessment.

Here is how we began our review of the 2014 assessment's draft chapter on human health:

> When [we] reviewed the 2009 draft Assessment, [we] stated that in [our] long career[s], of the many such documents [we] had reviewed, it was "by far the worst."

> That was then, this is now. The Human Health chapter is the worst single chapter [we] have ever read on climate change. It is littered with statements of "fact" that are easily challenged by the simplest observations. Here is an example from page 349:

> Some patients with mental illness are especially
> susceptible to heat (ref). Suicide varies seasonally
> (ref), suggesting potential climate impacts on
> depression.

OK. Are people more depressed in the South? Silly [us, we
were] under the impression that Seasonal Affective Disorder
is related to cold temperatures and short days. [We] stand
corrected.

Our review of the health chapter continued:

> [The chapter also says that] dementia is a risk factor for
> hospitalization and death during heat waves (ref). Patients
> with severe mental illness such as schizophrenia are at risk
> during hot weather related both to their illness (ref) and their
> medications (ref).

Therefore, more schizophrenia is expressed in the south and
in Arizona?

Further, according to the assessment:

> Additional potential mental health impacts, less
> well understood, include distress associated with
> environmental degradation (refs), and the anxiety
> and despair that knowledge of climate change
> might elicit in some people (ref).

You might add, "caused by scientists pushing insane
hypotheses as facts." How depressing! Some of the
government's pronouncements on global warming are able
to render even lukewarmers speechless.

The 2014 report's bias toward pessimism has implications throughout the federal regulatory process. It is cited (directly or indirectly)
as a primary source for the science of climate change and as justification for federal regulations aimed at mitigating greenhouse gas
emissions. Because the USGCRP gets it wrong, so do policymakers.
We noted systematic problems with the government's health effects
science in the Cato Institute 2012 addendum to the second National
Climate Assessment. The only difference between then and now is
that every new report since 2012 has characterized the health effects
of climate change as increasingly worse.

Both the second National Climate Assessment and our *ADDENDUM* have a chapter titled "Human Health" and each has "Key Messages." Here we alternate between the USGCRP and Cato documents:

USGCRP:

- Increases in the risk of illness and death related to extreme heat and heat waves are *very likely*. Some reduction in the risk of death related to extreme cold is expected.

ADDENDUM:

- The health effects of climate change on the United States are negligible today, and likely to remain so in the future, unless the United States goes into precipitous economic and technological decline.
- Death certificate data indicate that 46 percent of all deaths from extreme weather events in the United States from 1993 to 2006 were from excessive cold, 28 percent from excessive heat, 10 percent from hurricanes, 7 percent from floods, and 4 percent from tornadoes.
- Over the long term, deaths from extreme weather events have declined in the United States.
- Deaths in the United States peak in the colder months and are at a minimum in the warmer months.
- In U.S. cities, heat-related mortality declines as heat waves become stronger and more frequent.
- Census data indicate that the migration of Americans from the cold northern areas to the warmer southwest saves about 4,600 lives per year and is responsible for 3 to 7 percent of the gains in life expectancy from 1970 to 2000.

USGCRP:

- Some diseases transmitted by food, water, and insects are likely to increase.

ADDENDUM:

- While the U.S. Global Change Research Program chapter states that "Some diseases transmitted by food, water, and insects are likely to increase," incidence of these diseases have been reduced by orders of magnitude in the United States over the past century and show no sign of resurgence.

The government's dodgy climate-health work notwithstanding, the president claims a personal interest in the new initiative in blaming his daughter Malia's asthma on global warming. The idea is that global warming increases air pollution, which includes several irritants like ozone that may trigger asthma.

President Obama's own Environmental Protection Agency (EPA) notes that air pollution is in decline (by 33 percent since 1980, which includes Malia's entire lifetime and then some). The agency also cites the U.S. Heat Wave Index, which peaked 80 years ago during the Great Depression when the index was about an order of magnitude higher than it has been in the past decade (see Figure 37). Further, if global warming has increased the incidence of asthma in the past 20 years, how does that comport with the fact that, prior to the 2015–16 El Niño, and depending upon the temperature record, we had gone between 18 and 22 years without a significant trend in global temperature?[1]

Figure 37

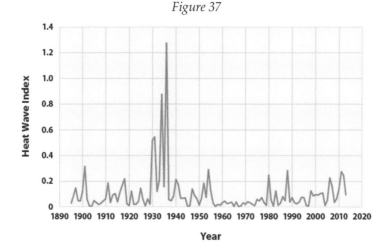

Note: EPA's Heat Wave Index clearly shows that the current era can't hold a candle to what happened in the 1930s.[2]

[1] We specifically exclude the two temperature histories produced by the (renamed) National Climatic Data Center and NASA that left out the satellite-sensed sea-surface temperatures and substituted hilariously inaccurate measurements from shipboard intake tubes, all in service of destroying "the pause" and just in time for the Paris summit. There is little chance these records will stand the test of time, especially after they are no longer needed to justify government policy.

[2] U.S. Environmental Protection Agency, "Climate Change Indicators in the United States, Third Edition," EPA 430-R-14-004, 2014, http://www.epa.gov/climatechange /pdfs/climateindicators-full-2014.pdf.

The USGCRP learned nothing from criticism of its heat-related mortality text in the 2009 report. It continues to forecast heat waves that lead to increasing numbers of deaths, even as the leading science says that more hot days actually will result in the opposite. By way of example, a 2014 article in *Nature Climate Change* shows that the impacts of extreme heat often are overplayed while the impacts of adaptation are underplayed. Another paper in *Environmental Health Perspectives* finds a declining risk of dying from heat waves in the United States for the past several decades. This also has been demonstrated in Europe and in major cities worldwide.[3, 4]

The idea that human-caused global warming is going to increase heat-related mortality simply is outdated and wrong. In fact, the opposite is true—a warming climate decreases the population's sensitivity to heat events because it induces adaptation. As we noted in *Nature Climate Change*:

> Some portion of this response [the decline in the risk of dying from heat waves] probably reflects the temporal increase in the frequency of extreme-heat events, an increase that elevates public consciousness and spurs adaptive response. In this manner, climate change itself leads to adaptation. . . . Our analysis highlights one of the many often-overlooked intricacies of the human response to climate change.[5]

But this information seems to fall on deaf ears, especially those at the USGCRP. Here is what USGCRP wrote concerning heat-related mortality in the executive summary of its 2014 extravaganza:

> Climate change will influence human health in many ways; some existing health threats will intensify, and new health threats will emerge. Some of the key drivers of health impacts include increasingly frequent and intense extreme heat, which causes heat-related illnesses and deaths and over time, worsens drought and wildfire risks, and intensifies air pollution.

---

[3] Paul C. Knappenberger et al., "Adaptation to Extreme Heat in Stockholm County, Sweden," *Nature Climate Change* 4 (2014): 302–3.

[4] Robert E. Davis et al., "Changing Heat-Related Mortality in the United States," *Environmental Health Perspectives* 111 (2003): 1712–18.

[5] Knappenberger et al., "Adaptation to Extreme Heat."

The EPA's 2009 endangerment finding concerning CO_2 expresses the same outlook (of course, since it is heavily based on USGCRP documents). EPA repeatedly emphasizes heat-related mortality as one of the major threats to public health as a justification of the need for CO_2 regulations.[6]

Here is what the agency has to say in its technical support document for its greenhouse gas endangerment finding: "*Severe heat waves are projected to intensify in magnitude and duration over the portions of the United States where these events already occur,* with potential increases in mortality and morbidity, especially among the elderly, young, and frail" [emphasis in original].

Compare the administration's take with what was published in 2014 by a research team led by Jennifer Bobb of Harvard University's School of Public Health. Bobb found that the risk of dying from excessive heat events is in decline across the United States and that most of the overall decline is due to declines in the sensitivity to extreme heat among the elderly population (those 75 and older). They also found that the risk in the older population has dropped so far that it now is indistinguishable from the risk to younger populations. Adaptation is a beautiful thing![7]

"While heat-related mortality risk for the ≥ 75 age group was greater than for the <65 age group at the beginning of the study period, by 2005 they had converged to similar levels," Bobb writes. In other words, depite all the administration's talk about the public health impact of an increasing threat from heat waves to the nation's growing elderly population, they simply have it wrong.

Bobb and her colleagues summarize the situation this way:

> This study provides strong evidence that acute (e.g., same-day) heat-related mortality risk has declined over time in the US, even in more recent years. This evidence complements findings from US studies using earlier data from the 1960s through mid-1990s on community-specific mortality rates [references], as well as European studies that found temporal declines in heat-related mortality risk [references], and supports the hypothesis that the population is continually adapting to heat.

[6] Even if Congress were to pass legislation prohibiting CO_2 regulation, presumably the president would veto it.

[7] Jennifer F. Bobb et al., "Heat-Related Mortality and Adaptation in the United States," *Environmental Health Perspectives* 122 (2014): 811–16.

We co-authored the two Davis studies cited above. Our work, published more than a decade ago, was among the first research demonstrating declining trends in heat-related mortality across the United States. We have been saying this for a long time, and the federal government has refused to listen for a long time. It's not what they want to hear.

The serial inaccuracies and misleading assertions resplendent in the USGCRP reports make lukewarmers suspicious of climate change assessment documents produced by an organization that benefits from a dire perception of climate change. The same can be said for the IPCC.

29. The Sexiest Storms on Earth

> Every time someone dies as a result of floods in Bangladesh, an airline executive should be dragged out of his office and drowned.

> —George Monbiot*

It's time we turn our attention to what some call extreme weather: hurricanes, floods, droughts, and tornadoes. Hurricanes are iconic. Each one that threatens landfall in the United States triggers a media circus. Pope Francis blames their occurrence on immoral economic activity in his 2015 encyclical, *Laudato Si'*. With regard to extreme weather, you'll see two divergent views. On one side, President Obama's administration and the Pope; on the other, lukewarm reality.

Tropical cyclones—called hurricanes in the Atlantic and eastern Pacific Oceans, typhoons in the western Pacific, and cyclones in the south Pacific and Indian Oceans—are beautiful, until you're in one. A mature tropical cyclone is brilliantly bright and features towering cumulonimbi surrounding an alluring eye. What could be prettier or more destructive? Near the eyewall of a Category 5 storm (one with sustained winds of more than 155 mph) the combination of kinetic energy and area affected makes for the strongest of any storm on Earth. Tropical cyclones are also strong attractors for both television cameras and climate campaigners.

There are no tropical cyclones in the eastern south Pacific and eastern south Atlantic oceans, thanks largely to cool upwelling. They're also extremely rare in the western south Atlantic—in fact, so rare that when one spins up, it's only hours before someone is blaming it on global warming.

---

* George Joshua Richard Monbiot is a British writer known for his political and environmental activism. We are quoting from the *Guardian* (UK).

After you scrape away some nagging details, tropical cyclones are pretty simple. Water evaporates at the sea's surface, rises, and condenses to form clouds. When anything changes from a less-ordered (gaseous) state to a more-ordered (liquid) one, energy is released to the surrounding environment. This is called "latent heat of condensation." If there's a lot of condensation, there's a lot of heat concentrated in a small region. Hot air rises, more moisture condenses out, more heat is released and—thanks to the rotation of the Earth—the column of clouds begins to spin faster and faster. When the winds exceed 74 miles per hour, you've got yourself a hurricane.

Everything else being equal (a dangerous concept in science), warmer oceans should evaporate more water. More water should condense in the form of clouds. More heat should be released, and the frequency or magnitude of tropical cyclones should increase. Makes sense, doesn't it? Well, actually, no it doesn't.

A strong tropical cyclone can't simply continue to send condensed moisture skyward. After the passage of some time, there's simply too much air over the top of the storm, and the upward motion becomes suppressed. Successful tropical cyclones require a venting mechanism high in the atmosphere to divert air away from its center. This is known as "outflow."

Moreover, tropical cyclones (or storms that are trying to become one) exist in a larger environment. If something destroys their inflow-outflow symmetry, a potential tropical cyclone can wind down to a pitiful batch of low-level clouds in as little as a day.

Enter El Niño!

El Niños slow (or even reverse) the easterly trade winds across the central Pacific Ocean. That effect cascades into everything from huge blizzards in the Sierra Nevada to blooming of the desert Southwest, drought in eastern Australia, and unemployment in the Peruvian anchovy fishery. An El Niño also is very mean to hurricanes. It generates a waft of unusual high-altitude westerly winds clear across the tropical Atlantic that kills a hurricane's outflow. That's why, in years when there's an El Niño (like 2015), the forecast is for a weak Atlantic hurricane season. While the number of Atlantic storms was nearly normal, a large number made landfall but caused very little damage.

A reigning myth is that El Niños somehow will become more frequent and stronger as the lower atmosphere warms due to the increasing concentration of atmospheric carbon dioxide caused by pernicious economic activity.

So, what will happen to hurricanes from a combination of increasing temperatures and increased frequency of El Niños?

We could consult the scientific literature and learn that storms may become stronger, but the changes may be so small that you won't notice them until sometime around 2080.[1, 2]

If we consult a different journal, we see research indicating fewer and weaker hurricanes are the probable result, or that altered atmospheric flow patterns will tend to steer them away from the U.S. east coast—which may explain why we have gone longer than ever between recorded Category 3 or higher (major hurricane) hits on the United States. The average time between landfalls of Category 3 or higher storms is around 800 days. As of mid-April 2016, we'd gone over 3,800 days since the last Category 3—Hurricane Wilma in southwest Florida in October 2005.[3, 4, 5]

Is it possible that global warming could reduce the likelihood of a major hurricane strike in the United States?

Hiroyuki Murakami of Japan's Meteorological Research Institute and a colleague at the University of Hawaii–Manoa, in 2010, compared the tracks of Atlantic basin tropical cyclones generated by a high-resolution climate model for a 25-year simulation of the present day with those of a future under the Intergovernmental Panel on

---

[1] Thomas R. Knutson and Robert E. Tuleya, "Impact of CO_2-Induced Warming on Simulated Hurricane Intensity and Precipitation: Sensitivity to the Choice of Climate Models and Convective Parameterization," *Journal of Climate* 17 (2004): 3477–95.

[2] Patrick J. Michaels et al., "Comments on 'Impacts of CO_2-Induced Warming on Simulated Hurricane Intensity and Precipitation: Sensitivity to the Choice of Climate Model and Convective Scheme,'" *Journal of Climate* 18 (2005): 5179–82, http://www.image.ucar.edu/idag/Papers/Michaels_commentsonmodeling.pdf.

[3] Philip J. Klotzbach, "El Niño–Southern Oscillation's Impact on Atlantic Basin Hurricanes and U.S. Landfalls," *Journal of Climate* 24 (2011): 1252–63.

[4] L. Bengtsson et al., "Will Greenhouse Gas-Induced Warming Lead to Higher Frequency of Hurricanes?" *Tellus* 48A (1996): 57–73.

[5] Wilma was the strongest Atlantic hurricane ever measured, sporting 185 mile per hour sustained winds and a lowest barometric pressure of 26.05 inches. Wilma's ferocious winds were, in part, due to the hurricane's exceedingly small eye—only 2.7 miles across. This kind of vortex is dynamically unstable. Within hours after reaching its October 19 peak, the eyewall was replaced, and Wilma subsided to a garden-variety Category 5 hurricane—the most destructive storms on Earth.

Climate Change midrange greenhouse gas–emissions scenario. They found a significant eastward shift in the tropical cyclone formation region in the Atlantic Ocean that resulted in decreased frequency of storms hitting the U.S. southeastern Atlantic and Gulf coasts along with a slight increase of strikes on the northeastern United States, but one so small that it doesn't nearly counter the decrease to the south and west.[6]

In follow-up work, using a newer version of their climate model, Murakami and 11 colleagues in 2012 found that, overall, the frequency of tropical cyclones approaching the U.S. coastline will decline by nearly 20 percent while the average maximum intensity of a storm approaching the coast will increase by one mile an hour, something no one could possibly notice in the midst of a tropical cyclone. More recently, James Elsner at Florida State University reports that global hurricane frequency has declined, but the average windspeed has risen by (are you sitting down?) three miles per hour in the past 30 years![7, 8]

For a textbook example of how climate scientists can exaggerate in the media, consider what appeared in the *Washington Post* on May 18, 2015:

> Since 1984 and the beginning of the enhanced satellite imagery era, the strength of hurricanes as measured by wind speed has increased by 3 miles per hour, but there were 6.1 fewer cyclones than there would have been if ocean temperatures would have remained unchanged.

> "We're seeing fewer hurricanes, but the ones we do see are more intense," said James Elsner, professor of geography at Florida State University and coauthor on the study. "When one comes, all hell can break loose."[9]

[6] Hiroyuki Murakami and Bin Wang, "Future Change of North Atlantic Tropical Cyclone Tracks: Projection by a 20-km-Mesh Global Atmospheric Model," *Journal of Climate* 23 (2010): 2699–721.

[7] Hiroyuki Murakami et al., "Future Changes in Tropical Cyclone Activity Projected by the New High-Resolution MRI-AGCM," *Journal of Climate* 25 (2012): 3237–60.

[8] Nam-Young Kang and James B. Elsner, "Trade-Off between Intensity and Frequency of Global Tropical Cyclones," *Nature Climate Change* 5 (2015): 661–64.

[9] Angela Fritz, "Global Warming Fueling Fewer but Stronger Hurricanes, Study Says," *Washington Post*, May 18, 2015, *Capital Weather Gang* blog at http://www.

Hurricanes are influenced by the magnitude of the Atlantic Warm Pool (AWP), basically the core subtropical surface temperature maximum that varies from year-to-year and from decade-to-decade. It's influenced by (what else but) El Niño and global warming.

Researchers Chunzai Wang and Sang-Ki Lee ascertained in 2008 that larger AWPs promote more intense hurricanes. But they later found, in 2011, that large AWPs alter atmospheric steering currents so the storms that do form have a tendency to curve northwards and remain out to sea without making landfall in the United States. Conversely, in years with small AWPs—a condition not favored by global warming—storms are steered more toward the southeastern Atlantic coast and Gulf of Mexico. Additionally, Wang claims, a "small but robust" reduction in landfalling hurricanes in the United States is in fact due to global warming making the vertical distribution of temperature somewhat less favorable than would otherwise be the case.[10, 11]

The lack of an observed long-term trend in the frequency or magnitude of hurricane landfalls in the United States—and the complete absence of recent Category 3 or stronger hurricanes making landfall in the past 10 years—increasingly appears to be consistent with a (luke)warmer world.[12]

In weather forecasting classes, students are taught what to do when different computer models yield conflicting results: look out the window to see what's happening. Perhaps climate scientists ought to do the same. If there's a massively conflicting literature concerning global warming and hurricanes striking the United States, look out your windows. The National Hurricane Center's Chris Landsea provides that window—the hurricane index shown in Figure 38. No trend whatsoever is apparent.

washingtonpost.com/blogs/capital-weather-gang/wp/2015/05/18/global-warming-fueling-fewer-but-stronger-hurricanes-study-says.

[10] Chunzai Wang and Sang-Ki Lee, "Global Warming and United States Landfalling Hurricanes," *Geophysical Research Letters* 35 (2008): L02708.

[11] Chunzai Wang et al., "Impact of the Atlantic Warm Pool on United States Landfalling Hurricanes," *Geophysical Research Letters* 38 (2011): L19702.

[12] These findings were ignored in 2014's National Climate Assessment. Lukewarmers become suspicious when things like this continue to happen.

Figure 38

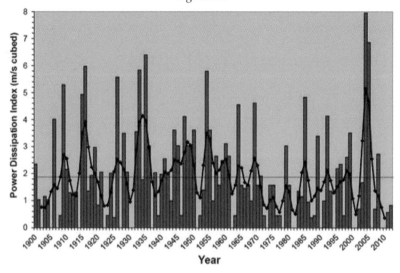

Note: The integrated power of hurricanes striking the United States shows no secular change at all.[13]

The role of tropical cyclones as iconic media stars was discovered in 1961 with Category 4 Hurricane Carla, one of the largest storms ever to hit the United States. Dan Rather—at the time a young reporter at CBS affiliate KHOU in Houston, Texas—began filing nightly dispatches from the seawall at Galveston, Texas. That city had been the site of the largest natural disaster in U.S. history—1900's Great Galveston Hurricane.

Strange as it may seem, before Hurricane Carla television networks had not realized the phenomenal power of a slow-moving killing machine with only marginal predictability. Ever since, egged on by cable television and the 24-hour news cycle, a good hurricane has the ability to become a lead news story, extending over the course of several days' broadcasting. The reason has little to do with the hurricane itself; rather, it is the demands imposed by this era's proliferation of 24-hour news programming.

[13] Christopher W. Landsea, "Meteorology: Hurricanes and Global Warming," *Nature* 438 (2005): E11–E12 and updates.

Every network and cable news outlet competes and is driven to find a sufficient number of talking heads to hold their audience's attention through the next commercial. The best way to do that is to manufacture controversy and dissent. An all-too-typical, on-air exchange might sound like this:

> Talking Head #1: Hurricanes are getting worse due to climate change. We know the oceans are getting warmer and that hurricanes feed on warm water.
>
> Talking Head #2: Actually, they're not. You ought to stop depending on what your computer tells you and look out the window.
>
> Talking Head #1: Of course you'd say something like that. You're a denialist and paid shill for industry. Did the Koch Brothers pay you to say that?
>
> Host: Stay tuned! We'll be right back with more on the dangers of Category 1 Hurricane Hype right after these messages from our sponsors.

Hurricane Sandy—which technically no longer was a hurricane when it buzzed into the Jersey Shore in 2012—was a terribly destructive cyclone. The story of its devastation totally captured every network and provided Al Gore, New York Governor Andrew Cuomo, and New York City Mayor Mike Bloomberg opportunities to blame it on dreaded global warming brought on by pernicious economic activity.

In addition to Landsea's U.S. hurricane power index (which goes back to 1900), we have global weather satellite coverage back to 1972, which means we can see each and every tropical cyclone since then. The satellite data can be used to estimate maximum winds. Since speed multiplied by time is a measure of kinetic energy, we also can look for any global or hemispheric trends in the integrated power of these storms.

Dr. Ryan Maue, of WeatherBELL Analytics LLC (a meteorological consulting firm), has done precisely that. He's compiled the Accumulated Cyclone Energy (ACE) index, a mathematical integration of storm wind-speed and longevity.

Figure 39

Note: Ryan Maue's Accumulated Cyclone Energy (ACE) index for the globe (blue circles), Northern Hemisphere (black circles), and Southern Hemisphere (area between the circles) shows no relationship between overall hurricane activity and global warming. The decided lack of signal is pretty lukewarm.[14]

Lukewarmers believe that even the most simple and obvious hypotheses (such as global warming will result in more or stronger hurricanes) must be tested against real-world data. If data don't support a hypothesis, it either must be modified or abandoned and, at least, retested.

Nature has had plenty of time to tell us how hurricanes respond to 75 years of rapidly increasing CO_2 emissions. They respond lukewarmly.

[14] Ryan Maue and WeatherBELL Analytics LLC, http://models.weatherbell.com /tropical.php.

170

30. How the U.S. Global Change Research Program Sees Hurricanes

If you torture the data long enough, it will confess.

—A statement likely attributable to every
responsible professor of statistics

The U.S. Global Change Research Program's (USGCRP) mission statement reads, "Thirteen Agencies, One Mission: Empower the Nation with Global Change Science." In the eyes of governments throughout history, empowerment often is synonymous with "indoctrinate." The section of the USGCRP's 2014 report on hurricanes is a case in point. Lukewarmers tend to suspect that indoctrination is under way when a large governmental entity cherry picks data on something as important as hurricanes.

Maue's Accumulated Cyclone Energy (ACE) index (Figure 39) isn't the only measure of hurricane activity. Kerry Emanuel at the Massachusetts Institute of Technology calculates something he calls the Power Dissipation Index (PDI). While ACE essentially integrates the square of wind speed (which is the actual physical relationship between speed and force), Emanuel's PDI represents the *cube* of wind speed. He does this, Emanuel says, because monetary losses in tropical cyclones are best related to the "third power of the wind."

Chapter 2 ("Our Changing Climate") in the USGCRP's 2014 National Climate Assessment contains a section on hurricanes. Tucked away in a sidebar is a history of Emanuel's PDI (Figure 40). The graphs begin in 1970 and end in 2009. Please note: There were four more hurricane seasons free of major U.S. landfalling hurricanes before the assessment's release in May 2014. The graphs include a trendline through the PDI data that begins in 1980. The trendline is upward and temperatures rise. So it's convenient for the authors to draw an association with human-caused global warming. But had they consulted a longer record, 1920–2013, for example (the last year for which data were available for their 2014 report), they easily could have ruled out any role for global warming.

Figure 40

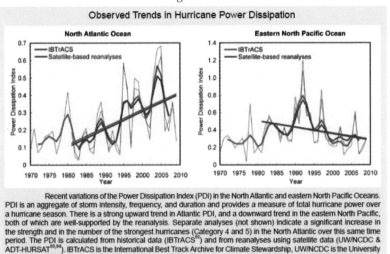

Observed Trends in Hurricane Power Dissipation

Recent variations of the Power Dissipation Index (PDI) in the North Atlantic and eastern North Pacific Oceans. PDI is an aggregate of storm intensity, frequency, and duration and provides a measure of total hurricane power over a hurricane season. There is a strong upward trend in Atlantic PDI, and a downward trend in the eastern North Pacific, both of which are well-supported by the reanalysis. Separate analyses (not shown) indicate a significant increase in the strength and in the number of the strongest hurricanes (Category 4 and 5) in the North Atlantic over this same time period. The PDI is calculated from historical data (IBTrACS[92]) and from reanalyses using satellite data (UW/NCDC & ADT-HURSAT[93,94]). IBTrACS is the International Best Track Archive for Climate Stewardship, UW/NCDC is the University of Wisconsin/NOAA National Climatic Data Center satellite-derived hurricane intensity dataset, and ADT-HURSAT is the Advanced Dvorak Technique–Hurricane Satellite dataset (Figure source: adapted from Kossin et al. 2007[95]).

Note: From the USGCRP's 2014 National Climate Assessment, *Climate Change Impacts in the United States*.[1]

The authors claim the ostensible reason for not using a longer record is that "there is considerable uncertainty in the record prior to the satellite era (early 1970s)." On the surface, this is true but at the same time, it's disingenuous. According to Chris Landsea, who helped develop the National Hurricane Center's Atlantic hurricane history data (known as HURDAT2), "Some storms were missed, and many intensities are too low in the pre-aircraft reconnaissance era (before 1944 in the western half of the basin) and in the pre-satellite era (before 1972 for the entire basin)."[2]

To state this differently, the PDI data prior to 1972 could be an underestimate, but it certainly isn't an overestimate.

For perspective, Ryan Maue provided us with the PDI record based upon the HURDAT2 data back to 1920. There's no significant trend when the record is examined, despite a warming of approximately 0.75°C in the earth's surface temperature history. Looked at that way,

[1] Jerry M. Melillo et al., eds., *Climate Change Impacts*, p. 42.

[2] Christopher W. Landsea and James L. Franklin, "Atlantic Hurricane Database Uncertainty and Presentation of a New Database Format," *Monthly Weather Review* 141 (2013): 3576–92.

the 2014 report's trendline (indicated in red in Figure 41) is nothing more than an absurd attempt to mislead people in "a key deliverable in President Obama's Climate Action Plan."

A voluminous literature supports the notion that periodic changes in the north-south temperature gradient in the Atlantic Ocean (the Atlantic Multidecadal Oscillation or AMO) are related to hurricane activity in the North Atlantic. According to Maue, the trendline in the 2014 National Climate Assessment begins during the negative phase of the AMO cycle (which promotes little hurricane activity) and ends during a positive phase (which favors high levels of hurricane activity). A more accurate assessment of hurricane activity would begin in 1950 (thereby reducing the influence of the AMO's cyclical nature). The result of doing that is a trend of zero (similar to the one beginning in 1920). But such data apparently are a distraction when one wants to paint an administration-preferred picture of the influence of anthropogenic climate change.

Figure 41

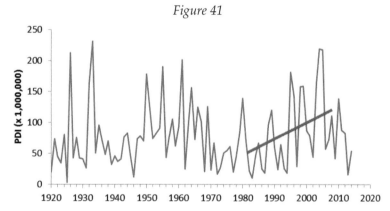

Note: Atlantic Basin Power Dissipation Index calculated from HURDAT2 by Ryan Maue. The USGCRP could have used this data extending through 2013 for its 2014 volume. The 1980–2009 trend as highlighted by the USGCRP appears in red.[3]

Lukewarmers believe climatic data sets should be viewed in their entirety, not cherry-picked.

🌀🌀🌀🌀🌀

[3] Ryan Maue, http://models.weatherbell.com/news/atlantic_ace_pdi.dat. Analysis by the authors.

31. Typhoon Haiyan: "Man Has Slapped Nature in the Face"

> There is not a building in town that is uninjured. Hundreds are busy day and night clearing away the debris and recovering the dead. It is awful. Every few minutes a wagon load of corpses passes by on the street.
>
> —John D. Blagden (Galveston, Texas, 1900)*

Politicians have been known to use weather disasters to further their political agenda. Will anyone forget New Jersey Governor Chris Christie giving President Barack Obama a giant hug after the remnants of Hurricane Sandy devastated the North Jersey shore in 2012? The president could not have been more pleased to have scored B-roll of yet another weather extreme his administration might conflate with global warming. Even Pope Francis who, like Obama, views global warming as the most important environmental story on Earth, took advantage of 2013's Typhoon Haiyan in service of his agenda.[1]

On November 3, 2013, near the end of the most active typhoon season in the western Pacific since 1994, a low-pressure system developed about 50 miles north of the island of Pohnpei about halfway between the Marshall Islands and Guam. Within a day it had reached tropical storm status with sustained winds of more than 38 mph. It

---

* This is from an account of the Great Galveston Hurricane of 1900 by John D. Blagden, an employee of the U.S. Weather Bureau in Galveston, Texas. The death tolls in the Galveston hurricane and Typhoon Haiyan were very similar.

[1] Technically, Sandy was not a hurricane when it made landfall in northeast New Jersey on October 29, 2012. It had lost its tropical cyclone characteristics and had come to more resemble a gigantic winter cyclone. Several things conspired to make Sandy so large. It came together very late in the hurricane season, when storms tend to be large. A very active jet stream poured in plenty of cold Canadian air from the north and west. It snowed from West Virginia to the Jersey beaches after the storm came ashore. None of this bears any relation to global warming.

175

was designated Haiyan and became Typhoon Haiyan the next day when sustained wind speeds were clocked at more than 73 mph.

Haiyan came to life smack dab in the middle of the most favorable environment on Earth for tropical cyclone development—over some of the warmest open-ocean water on the planet. With strong outflow aloft and no nearby land to cut off Haiyan's moisture supply and distort its heat engine, the tropical cyclone quickly developed into a Category 5 typhoon with sustained winds exceeding 155 mph. On November 6, 2013, Haiyan damaged every home on Kayangel, a northern Palau island.

Typhoon Haiyan then accelerated west-northwestward and posted its maximum estimated sustained wind of 196 mph. Twenty-four hours later, it smashed ashore at Tacloban City, on Leyte in the Philippines. An accompanying massive storm surge flooded into the extensive and densely populated lowlands. Ninety percent of Tacloban was destroyed. The Philippine government estimates total fatalities at 6,300 from Haiyan's onshore impact and from upland flooding. That's a modern record for the island nation.[2]

Nation magazine was convinced Haiyan had been goosed by global warming. Hurricane historian Ryan Maue doesn't agree. He notes that while there have been 58 super-typhoons since 1950 (ones whose lowest barometric pressure falls below 26.58 inches), only eight have occurred in the past 25 years.[3, 4]

Pope Francis has gotten religion on global warming. The Pope's encyclical *Laudato Si'* concerning care for our common home and, in part, about the environment and climate change, was released on June 18, 2015. The Pope planned to attend the annual UN

[2] The estimate of 196 mph winds comes from the U.S. Joint Typhoon Warning Center and was calculated using satellite data. Hurricane-hunter aircraft don't fly into Pacific typhoons. In 1969, one of those reconnaissance flights recorded data resulting in an estimate of 202 mph sustained winds in Hurricane Camille, then only 140 miles southeast of New Orleans. The world record for a three-second gust (as opposed to a sustained wind) is 253 mph (!) in the eyewall of Typhoon Olivia as it passed over Australia's Barrow Island on April 10, 1996.

[3] Walden Bello and Foreign Policy in Focus, "Yes, Typhoon Haiyan Was Caused by Climate Change: The Super-Typhoon That Just Hit the Philippines Should Be a Wake-Up Call for Climate Change Negotiators in Warsaw," *Nation*, November 11, 2013, http://www.thenation.com/blog/177111/yes-typhoon-haiyan-was-caused-climate-change#.

[4] Ryan Maue, Twitter post, November 16, 2013, 8:49 p.m., https://twitter.com/RyanMaue/status/401934987605209088.

ambassadorial conference on global warming in New York the day after addressing a joint session of the U.S. Congress on September 24. In December, it was expected he would travel to the 21st Conference of the Parties (COP-21) in Paris, France, and lend his moral authority on climate change to President Barack Obama's political authority.[5]

En route to celebrating Mass with an estimated half-million people in Tacloban in January 2015, Pope Francis said global warming is mostly man-made because "it is man who has slapped nature in the face." His homily deemed Typhoon Haiyan (or Yolanda, as it is known in the Philippines) "the strongest storm ever recorded on Earth." His visit was cut short by another, much weaker typhoon that was bearing down on the Philippines.[6]

Lukewarmers know that severe weather is a characteristic of earth's atmosphere and that every day some kind of storm or extreme event can (and likely will) be associated with global warming. Lukewarmers also know that if the issue of the day were global cooling, such extreme weather events could be made to fit that paradigm, too.

[5] John Vidal, "Pope Francis's Edict on Climate Change Will Anger Deniers and U.S. Churches: Pontiff Hopes to Inspire Action at Next Year's Meeting in Paris in December after Visits to the Philippines and New York," *Guardian* (U.K.), December 27, 2014, http://www.theguardian.com/world/2014/dec/27/pope-francis-edict-climate-change-us-rightwing.

[6] We'll note that the Pope's homily departed radically from the prepared text. Pope Francis chose to omit references to global warming and instead spoke to the suffering of his flock.

32. Are Floods Increasing?

> Entire nations could be wiped off the face of the earth by rising sea levels if global warming is not reversed by the year 2000. Coastal flooding and crop failures would create an exodus of "eco-refugees," threatening political chaos, said Brown, director of the New York office of the U.N. Environment Program. He said governments have a 10-year window of opportunity to solve the greenhouse effect.
>
> —Associated Press (June 30, 1989)

Hurricanes generally are pretty bad news. That's due in part to their propensity to produce massive flooding. In fact, there are far greater fatalities from a hurricane's floods than there are from its ferocious winds. But hurricanes aren't the only thing that can cause a flood. A big thunderstorm will, too. Like hurricanes, they are fueled by atmospheric moisture.

Cold air is incapable of holding much moisture. That's why your skin gets so dry in winter. Warm air is able to hold a lot more, which is why Washington, D.C., can become unbearably awful in most summers. It follows that if there's more moisture around, there should be more rain, which will cause streamflow to increase. A pedestrian term for extreme streamflow is "flood." If all of this is so, then a globally warmed atmosphere should increase flooding rains. It's obvious, isn't it?

Lukewarmers have a tendency to question things so seemingly climatically obvious.

If changes in streamflow are related to long-term changes in climate, and one accepts that the majority of that change is caused by enhanced CO_2, then human activity should increase streamflow and flood frequency. At least that's the position of the Intergovernmental Panel on Climate Change concerning post-1950 climate.

Gregory McCabe and David Wolock, scientists with the U.S. Geological Survey, recently examined historical streamflow records (1951–2009) from 516 rivers and streams they considered to be minimally impacted by human development. They first sorted the data into regional patterns. Then they compared the temporal behavior of those patterns with common historical climate indices such as well-known patterns of atmospheric circulation, sea-surface temperature, and (yes) even global warming.[1]

They were unable to find many meaningful relationships between streamflow and the larger atmospheric phenomena. There were so very few that they hardly were worth mentioning.

Here's how McCabe and Wolock describe what they (didn't) find:

> Comparing time series of climate indices . . . with the time series of mean [stream] flow for the 14 clusters [patterns] indicates weak correlations that are statistically significant for only a few clusters. These results indicate that most of the temporal variability in streamflow in the conterminous U.S. is unpredictable in terms of relations to well-known climate indices.

In other words, trends and variability in larger-scale features of the climate (including rising temperature due to global warming) are not strongly (if at all) related to regional and temporal character-istics of streamflow across the United States.

The two researchers also considered the direct (local) effect of global warming—that warmer air holds more moisture and thus it could theoretically rain more frequently and harder. But they found very few long-term trends indicative of steadily rising moisture lev-els. Instead, they found the historical records to be dominated by periods of multidecadal variability. In their words:

> Analyses of the annual mean streamflow time series for the 14 streamflow clusters indicated periods of extended wet and dry periods, but did not indicate any strong monotonic trends. Thus, the mean cluster streamflow time series indicate nearly random variability with some periods of persistence.

---

[1] Gregory J. McCabe and David M. Wolock, "Spatial and Temporal Patterns in Con-terminous United States Streamflow Characteristics," *Geophysical Research Letters* 41 (2014): 6889–97.

Figure 42

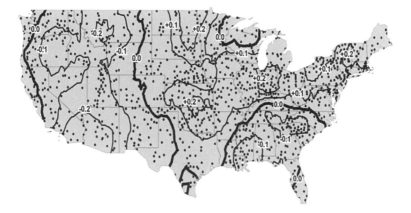

Note: Correlation between year and precipitation, 1979–2009.[2]

The bottom line is that McCabe and Wolock couldn't identify any behavior in historical streamflow records that is suggestive of an influence from human-caused global warming. The year-to-year statistical noise in the flood data overwhelms any weak signal caused by lukewarming.

There isn't much of any signal in U.S. precipitation data as the planet warmed. Figure 42 displays the correlation between year and rainfall since 1979. Statistically speaking, the amount of variation that is explained by the correlation coefficient is its squared value. For example, the correlation coefficients of around −0.2 that appear in the desert southwest mean that only 4 percent (−0.2 x −0.2) of the year-to-year variation is explained by time, which (in a warming world) is obviously a proxy for warming.

So the next time you hear that floods are increasing in the United States and that it is "consistent with global warming" (using some convoluted explanation), ask why there is no linkage between streamflow and global warming.

[2] Robert C. Balling Jr. and Gregory B. Goodrich, "Spatial Analysis of Variations in Precipitation Intensity in the USA," *Theoretical and Applied Climatology* 104 (2011): 415–21.

Figure 43

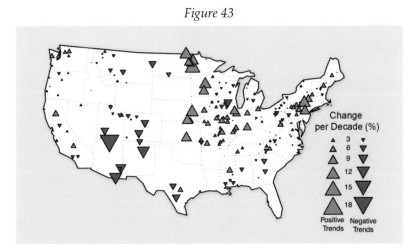

Note: From the U.S. Global Change Program third National Climate Assessment *Climate Change Impacts in the United States* (2014), citing Hirsch and Ryberg.[3]

This reality doesn't faze the U.S. Global Change Research Program. In the "water" section of its 2014 report, "Key Message #3" is "Increased risk of flooding in many parts of the U.S." It goes on to state that *"significant* changes" in annual precipitation and soil moisture will affect annual flood magnitudes "in many regions" [emphasis added].[4]

It appears that the assessment's authors may only have looked at the pictures (see Figure 43). Here's how Hirsch and Ryberg summarize their findings:

> What these results do indicate is that except for the decreased flood magnitudes observed in the SW, there is no strong empirical evidence in any of the other 3 regions for increases or decreases in flood magnitudes in the face of the 32% increase in GMCO2 [global mean carbon dioxide concentration] that has taken place over the study period.

[3] Jerry M. Melillo et al., eds., *Climate Change Impacts*; R. M. Hirsch and K. R. Ryberg, "Has the Magnitude of Floods across the USA Changed with Global CO_2 Levels?" *Hydrological Sciences Journal* 57 (2012): 1–9.

[4] See Chapter 21c of this book. According to the USGCRP's models, the average time to detect a significant precipitation change will be around 300 years from now.

We've examined some rainfall data, too, and found a significant increase in rainfall on the rainiest days of the year in the Northeast, but nothing of note elsewhere. As we wrote earlier, there's no demonstrable increase (or decrease) in weather-related damages once population and property values are accounted for, so whatever changes there are in rainfall nationally, they are inconsequential.[5]

Lukewarmers realize that there's a great deal of variability in global and national precipitation data. Finding any signal in such noisy data that can be related to global warming is very difficult. Absent such a signal, there can be no cause and effect.

---

[5] Patrick J. Michaels et al., "Trends in Precipitation on the Wettest Days of the Year across the Contiguous USA," *International Journal of Climatology* 24 (2004): 1873–82.

33. Tornado Warning!

> All weather events occur in the context of natural variability
> and the changing climate.
>
> —Dr. Paul Epstein*

A horrific tornado ripped an 81-mile path through central Alabama, running from Tuscaloosa to Birmingham, on April 27, 2011. It made a direct hit on the University of Alabama campus and was part of a multistate outbreak that killed 316 people. The last time more people were killed on a single tornado day was March 18, 1925, when the infamous Tri-State Tornado tore its way from Missouri to Indiana.

Less than a month later, in May 2011, another monster touched down in northern Missouri and killed 160 people in Joplin. The late Paul Epstein, writing in *Atlantic* said, "This uptick in severe twisters is a new phenomenon."[1]

Lukewarmers prefer data to anecdote.

Are there really more strong tornadoes? The answer is easily determined thanks to the painstaking work of the late Tetsuya Fujita who, in the course of a decades-long study, catalogued every tornado report for 50 years (Figure 44). He developed the popular F (for Fujita) scale, with numbers F3 through F5 labeled as "severe" to "incredible."

Monster tornadoes don't get missed. If there were an increase in their number, it would be obvious. Paul Epstein, preparing his article for *Atlantic*, could have looked up the numbers with a few mouse-clicks.

---

*Paul R. Epstein (1943–2011) was a physician and associate director of the Harvard Medical School's Center for Health and the Global Environment and a widely quoted alarmist with regard to climate and health. We nominate his 2011 quote from "An Era of Tornadoes: How Global Warming Causes Wild Winds" in *Atlantic* magazine as the "Karl Popper Memorial Pseudoscience Statement of 2011." It is simply unfalsifiable.

[1] Paul Epstein, "An Era of Tornadoes: How Global Warming Causes Wild Winds," *Atlantic*, July 8, 2011, http://www.theatlantic.com/international/archive/2011/07/an-era-of-tornadoes-how-global-warming-causes-wild-winds/241639.

Figure 44

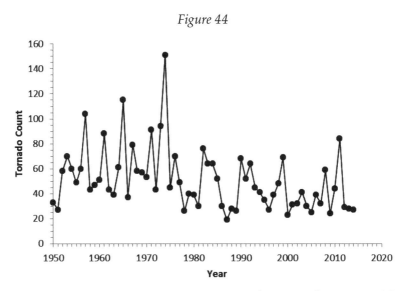

Note: Number of severe or stronger tornadoes (F3–F5 on the Fujita scale). Clearly there is no increase in their frequency, even as the total number of reported tornadoes has more than doubled, thanks to radar detection.[2]

Tornado-wise, there's nothing new nowadays. Midday on May 11, 1953, 114 people perished in a Waco, Texas, tornado. Another 116 died in Flint, Michigan, on June 8. Ninety-four more were killed the next day in Worcester, Massachusetts.

The Flint and Worcester tornadoes very likely were caused by the same long-lived, super-cell thunderstorm—the same type of thing that traveled 300 miles in 2011 and spun up the Tuscaloosa, Alabama, disaster. A single storm in Tupelo, Mississippi, killed 216 people in 1936. The next day, on April 5, another 203 were killed in Gainesville, Georgia.

It's not the frequency of super storms that's changed in the past century; there now are a lot more people and property in harm's way. So (here's that dread phrase again) everything else being equal, the number of fatalities should be increasing. Yet despite what happened in 2011, there's strong evidence that a tremendous number of lives are being saved using modern technology. Now that's a story

[2] Storm Prediction Center, National Oceanic and Atmospheric Administration, http://www.spc.noaa.gov/wcm. Analysis by the authors.

that warms lukewarmers' hearts because it shows how modern society adapts to the vagaries of weather and climate.

After the 1953 disasters, University of Chicago's David Atlas (the developer of weather radar) convinced Congress to support a national network of detectors known as the WSR-57 (for 1957), a very useful machine for picking up tornadoes capable of causing significant damage. By the mid-1970s, WSR-57s pretty much covered all of the nation's tornado-prone regions. Two significant things happened. First, the number of reported tornadoes increased. Before WSR-57 went online, the number averaged about 500 per year. When the network was complete, the number we could detect leveled out around 800. Second, the tornado death rate (or number of fatalities per million population) dropped precipitously. This is an example of unqualified and successful technological adaptation to one of nature's most dangerous storms.

In the late 1980s, a new Doppler radar system was deployed. Called WSD-88, it is able to track the movement of air within a storm. In doing so, it enables meteorologists to pinpoint a tornado's vortex. Once again, the number of tornadoes soared due in large part to the detection of hundreds of F0 storms (that's F-zero, what we might call "twisties") able to knock over an untethered trailer or the sign at Bob's Grille in Nags Head, North Carolina, but little else. We now average over 1,000 per year, a number that has been constant since the Doppler network went national. Death frequencies dropped a bit more, but not as much as they did from WSR-57's deployment, which picked the low-hanging fruit. While we save more lives, we also detect more weenie storms.[3]

Moore, a suburb of Oklahoma City, Oklahoma, is the undisputed severe tornado capital of the world. The community experienced an extreme F5 tornado in 1999. It was the most powerful ever measured and barreled a long path through suburban sprawl, killing 36 people. There have been two more F5s in Moore since then.

As tragic as 36 deaths are at a personal level, one must ask, "Why was the number so low?" That storm easily could have killed 1,000.

To begin with, Oklahoma City, Oklahoma, is tornado-nuts (in a good way because, well, it should be). The National Severe Storms Laboratory is located there for a very good reason: it is able to

---

[3] That sign for Bob's Grille says, "Eat and get the hell out."

conduct a lot of field research. Local television stations compete with one another in storm tracking. Many of them employ their own Doppler radar.

In the absence of modern technology and hyperawareness, that F5 in 1999 would have killed many more than 36 people. We see the same story with tornadoes as we experience concerning urban heat waves: the more frequent they are, the fewer people are harmed.

The remarkable and good news is that the frequency of tornado fatalities, in deaths per million, has been cut at least fourfold in the past century (Figure 45).

Tornado death-rate statistics indicate that people have adapted to the most intense storms on Earth. Surely we can adapt to a degree or two of warming.

Lukewarmers know that humans adapt to the vagaries of climate each and every day, and will do so into the future.

Figure 45

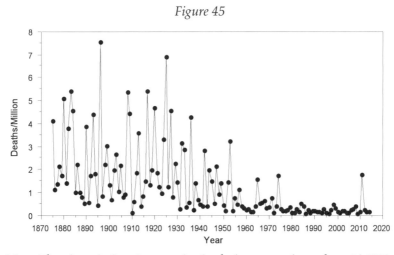

Note: The slow decline in tornado death frequency from the mid-1920s through the early-1950s was greatly accelerated through deployment of weather radar in the 1950s and 1960s.[4]

[4] Storm Prediction Center, National Oceanic and Atmospheric Administration, http://www.spc.noaa.gov/wcm. Analysis by the authors.

34. Quiz Time: Damages from Extreme Weather

> Not long ago, hurricanes, tornadoes, floods, drought, forest fires, even earthquakes and volcanic explosions were accepted as "natural disasters" or "acts of God." But now, we have joined God, powerful enough to influence these events.
>
> —David Suzuki*

It's time for a multiple-choice quiz. Who wrote, "There is medium evidence and high agreement that long-term trends in normalized losses [from extreme weather] have not been attributed to natural or anthropogenic climate change"?[1]

a) Someone who knows how to write
b) The Koch Brothers
c) Cato Institute
d) UN Intergovernmental Panel on Climate Change

Obviously, the answer can't be (a). It's not likely to be (b) either because Charles and David Koch write and speak eloquently. Such a poorly constructed sentence would not make it past Cato Institute editors, so that rules out (c). Which leaves (d).

That's right. The sentence appears in a recent report on climate extremes published under the auspices of the UN. Because the UN couldn't come right out and say it (clearly), it's up to others to translate

---

* David Suzuki is a professor emeritus at the University of British Columbia (Canada), academic, broadcaster, and environmental activist.

[1] J. Handmer et al., "Changes in Impacts of Climate Extremes: Human Systems and Ecosystems," in *Managing the Risks of Extreme Events and Disasters to Advance Climate Change Adaptation: A Special Report of Working Groups I and II of the Intergovernmental Panel on Climate Change (IPCC)* (New York: Cambridge University Press, 2012), pp. 231–90.

Figure 46

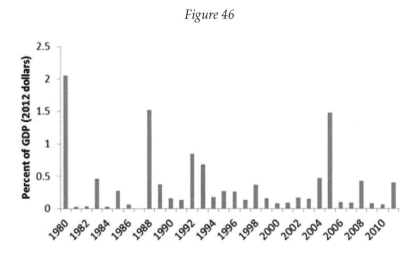

Note: The cost of U.S. weather disasters as a percentage of gross domestic product isn't increasing.[2]

the sentence into colloquial English: "Any trends in weather-related losses are not likely related to global warming." Weather-related damages are not increasing as a percentage of gross domestic product (see Figure 46). When more stuff is produced, thereby increasing GDP, more stuff becomes available to be hit by bad weather.

[2] GDP data from Bureau of Economic Analysis, U.S. Department of Commerce, http://www.bea.gov/national. Billion-dollar weather disaster data from National Centers for Environmental Information, National Oceanic and Atmospheric Administration, http://www.ncdc.noaa.gov/billions/events. Analysis by the authors.

35. Polar Ice Extent: A Tale of Two Hemispheres

> Arctic specialist Bernt Balchen says a general warming trend over the North Pole is melting the polar ice cap and may produce an ice-free Arctic Ocean by the year 2000.

—*Christian Science Monitor* (June 8, 1972)

Figure 47

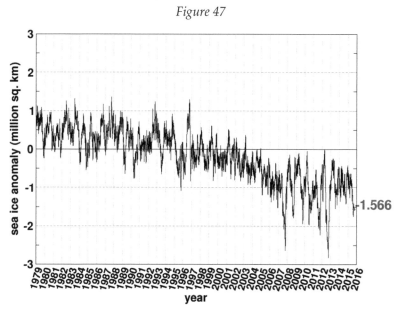

Note: Northern Hemisphere sea ice departures from the 1979–2008 mean.[1]

---

[1] From the website *The Cryosphere Today*, "Northern Hemispheric Anomaly" prepared by the Polar Research Group, Department of Atmospheric Sciences, University of Illinois at Urbana–Champaign, http://arctic.atmos.uiuc.edu/cryosphere/IMAGES/seaice.anomaly.arctic.png.

At first glance, OMG, the North Pole is melting!

Satellites in polar orbit can sense the presence of ice versus water by measuring microwave radiation. The first data from the Scanning Multichannel Microwave Radiometer (SMMR) satellite was launched in late 1978. That's 37 years ago, and the late 1970s were an interesting time in our climate history.

Approximately a decade before, the first attempts were made to create a global temperature history from surface weather stations. They showed a sharp warming from the early 20th century (when recordkeeping began) to roughly 1950. The sharp rise in temperature was followed by a steep, comparable fall. That plunge in temperature begat fears of global cooling, glib pronouncements about a coming ice age, and a breathless article on global cooling and a possible food crisis in the April 28, 1975, edition of *Newsweek*.[2, 3, 4]

The temperature immediately began to rise. Nonetheless, the expansion of Arctic ice was among the rationales for sending the microwave sounders into orbit.

---

[2] George J. Kukla and Alois Koči, "End of the Last Interglacial in the Losses Record," *Quaternary Research* 2 (1972): 374–83.

[3] Reid A. Bryson and Thomas J. Murray, *Climates of Hunger: Mankind and the World's Changing Weather* (Madison: University of Wisconsin Press, 1977).

[4] According to *Newsweek*:

> There are ominous signs that the Earth's weather patterns have begun to change dramatically and that these changes may portend a drastic decline in food production with serious political implications for just about every nation on Earth. The drop in food output could begin quite soon, perhaps only 10 years from now. The regions destined to feel its impact are the great wheat-producing lands of Canada and the U.S.S.R. in the north, along with a number of marginally self-sufficient tropical areas—parts of India, Pakistan, Bangladesh, Indochina and Indonesia—where the growing season is dependent upon the rains brought by the monsoon.

> The evidence in support of these predictions has now begun to accumulate so massively that meteorologists are hard-pressed to keep up with it. In England, farmers have seen their growing season decline by about two weeks since 1950, with a resultant overall loss in grain production estimated at up to 100,000 tons annually.

Figure 48

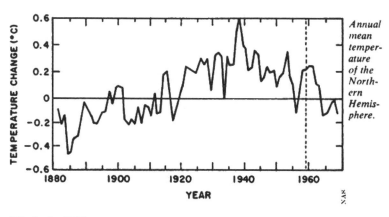

March 1, 1975

Note: The National Academy of Sciences's 1975 report, *Understanding Climate Change*, contains this plot of Northern Hemisphere temperatures. Changes in temperature were even greater at high latitudes.[5]

High latitude northern hemisphere data from the temperature history produced by the Climate Research Unit at the University of East Anglia shows 1970s summer temperatures to have been the coldest since the 1920s. Consequently, when the satellites first began recording sea ice data, the Arctic Ocean's ice extent must have been anomalously high. This suggests that some of the subsequent decline in Arctic ice extent is a result of natural variability (assuming the 1970s cold to have been natural). Therefore, it appears that about half of

[5] National Academy of Sciences, United States Committee for the Global Atmospheric Research Program, *Understanding Climate Change: A Program for Action* (Washington, D.C.: National Academy of Sciences, 1975).

the changes in Arctic ice extent since the satellites' launch have been caused by things other than human-induced global warming.[6, 7, 8]

Two interesting developments begin around 2007: the decline in Arctic sea ice extent ceases and within-year variability becomes much greater. This is expected with a general thinning of the ice. At the winter's end, all of the Arctic Ocean is ice covered, no matter what the temperature. Greenhouse gases simply can't sufficiently warm up the ocean to keep its surface liquid under months of polar night. But if the ice is thinner, it should melt more rapidly in the summer and create a greater winter/summer difference over time. There's very weak evidence at the end of the graph in Figure 49 indicating the sea ice may have thickened up a little, but there are not enough data to say anything definitive. The hiatus in the decline supports the notion that some of the overall decline came from some internal oscillation, which now is reversed and countering the effect of warming.

The ice sensing satellites are in polar orbit. About two hours after they've scanned the North Pole, they're over Antarctica.

Despite their abysmally cold winters, the Arctic and Antarctic are remarkably dissimilar. The North Pole is in the middle of an ocean almost exactly the size of Antarctica. The South Pole is in the middle

[6] V. A. Semenov and M. Latif, "The Early Twentieth Century Warming and Winter Arctic Sea Ice," *The Cryosphere* 6 (2012): 1231–37.

[7] The latest version of the temperature history is HadCRUT4, first released in 2012.

[8] According to the UN Intergovernmental Panel on Climate Change, *Climate Change 2013: The Physical Science Basis*:

> Anthropogenic forcings are very likely to have contributed to Arctic sea ice loss since 1979. . . . Arctic temperature anomalies in the 1930s were apparently as large as those in the 1990s and 2000s.

> It is difficult to untangle the relative roles of human-induced climate change versus natural variability in causing the Arctic sea ice decline. Using climate model simulations from the NCAR CCSM4 . . . inferred that approximately half (56%) of the observed rate of decline from 1979 to 2005 was externally (anthropogenically) forced, with the other half associated with natural internal variability. [Reference] used multiple climate model simulations from CMIP5 to infer that approximately 60% of the observed rate of decline from 1979–2011 is externally forced (compared to 41% determined from the earlier CMIP3 simulations). These simulations suggest an important role for natural variability as well as for human-induced climate change; further clarification of their relative roles awaits improved capabilities of the climate models in simulating natural internal variability, improved historical records of solar variability, and a longer record of sea ice extent.

of a landmass the size of the Arctic Ocean. In this way they are, literally, polar opposites.

Antarctica is so cold that there's very little melting in summer (except in the narrow Antarctic Peninsula stretching northward toward Tierra del Fuego, the southernmost tip of South America). So any changes in Antarctic sea ice extent take place at the continental margin, quite a distance from the South Pole.

There's plenty of ice in the Arctic Ocean, even in the beginning of fall when it reaches its minimum extent. But at the end of Austral

Figure 49

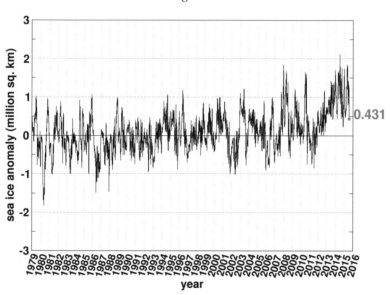

Note: Southern Hemisphere sea ice departures from the 1979–2000 average. The satellite data show a statistically significant upward trend in Antarctic sea ice.[9]

[9] From the website *The Cryosphere Today*, "Southern Hemispheric Anomaly," prepared by the Polar Research Group, Department of Atmospheric Sciences, University of Illinois at Urbana–Champaign, http://arctic.atmos.uiuc.edu/cryosphere/IMAGES/seaice.anomaly.antarctic.png.

summer, the lion's share of Antarctic ice retreats all the way to the continental margin (Figure 49) except where the ocean reaches farthest south in the Weddell Sea.

In the past few years, the departure from normal in the Northern Hemisphere ice extent (~ –1.3 million square kilometers) has been balanced by the gain in the Southern Hemisphere. However, that's not the case across the entire record. Declines in the north tend to be a bit larger than gains in the south.

In 2015, a team of three Chinese scientists compared the observed and forecast trends in Southern Hemisphere sea ice. To those who say, "The science is settled," their findings (in Figure 50) should prove somewhat unsettling.

Figure 50

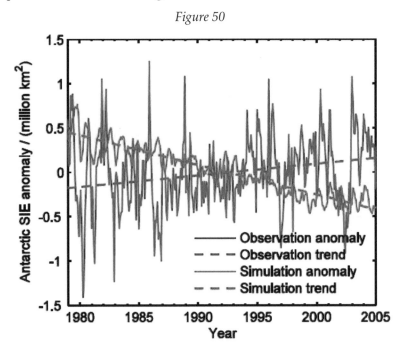

Note: Comparison of observed (blue) and mean climate model projected (red) changes in Antarctic sea ice extent (SIE).[10]

[10] Q. Shu et al., "Assessment of Sea Ice Simulations in the CMIP5 Models," *The Cryosphere* 9 (2015): 399–409.

While the decline in Northern Hemisphere sea ice extent is consistent with what has been forecast by climate models, the rise in the Southern Hemisphere is not. Lukewarmers are concerned that we clearly don't understand this part of the climate puzzle—and it's a very large part.

Arctic ice has declined before, even in the last century before humans had put very much CO_2 into the atmosphere. Here's what the *Washington Post* had to say about that on November 11, 1922:

> The Arctic Ocean is warming up, icebergs are growing scarcer and in some places the seals are finding the water too hot. Reports from fishermen, seal hunters and explorers . . . all point to a radical change in climate conditions and hitherto unheard-of temperatures in the Arctic zone. Great masses of ice have been replaced by moraines of earth and stones . . . while at many points well-known glaciers have entirely disappeared. Very few seals and no white fish are found in the eastern Arctic, while vast shoals of herring and smelts, which have never before ventured so far north, are being encountered in the old seal fishing grounds.

36. Death of the Polar Bear?

> If we don't change the path we are on now, then it will be too
> late. Polar bears will become extinct.

> —Kassie Siegel*

According to numerous records ranging from ice cores to assemblages of buried tree pollen, the end of the last ice age is thought to be around 10,800 years ago. At the time, thanks to Earth's orbital precession, our planet was closest to the sun during Northern Hemisphere summer. It now is closest in Northern Hemisphere *winter,* which means the high latitudes of our hemisphere received about 7 percent more solar radiation 11,000 years ago. Back then, that was enough to provoke a series of events that debunk a lot of global warming scare stories—especially the ones concerning the extinction of polar bears that, by the way, are not cute, little animals. They are dangerous and ferocious.[1, 2]

That seemingly slight change in solar input had the effect of dramatically warming the high-latitude Northern Hemisphere summer far beyond anything humans might accomplish anytime soon. The alterations in high-latitude ecosystems were striking. Consider what happened in Eurasia.

Today, the boreal forest (AKA "the north woods") extends to within about 150 miles of the Arctic Ocean. North of the forest is a treeless tundra, basically an Arctic desert. Both tundra and boreal forest soils are very acidic. A tree growing on the border between

---

*Kassie Siegel is senior counsel and director of the Center of Biological Diversity's Climate Law Institute.

[1] If the standard definition of ice age is "an extended period with expansive glaciers and ice caps displaced far from polar regions," 10,000 feet of ice atop much of Greenland (with its southern tip extending below latitude 60°N) could argue that we have been in a continuous ice age for the past 1.5 million years.

[2] A. Berger and M. F. Loutre, "Insolation Values for the Climate of the Last 10 Million Years," *Quaternary Science Reviews* 10 (1991): 297–317.

them eventually will fall into what resembles a peat bog and be preserved until the next glaciation.

Between 6,000 and 9,000 years ago, the northern forest extended all the way to the Arctic Ocean. We know this because of our ability to carbon-date trees we find buried there. The ocean itself was smaller, thanks to a larger volume of land ice than is there today. Even the presently barren island of Nova Zemlya in the Arctic Ocean north of European Russia (where the 50-megaton *Tsar Bomba* was detonated) and Wrangel Island (about 100 miles from the northeastern corner of Siberia) were tree covered.

The forest's northern limit is defined by summer temperature. The forest extending all the way to the ocean during this period means that July temperatures were as much as 7°C (12.6°F) warmer than their 20th century average.[3]

So despite all of the hand-wringing about "irreversible changes" in the Arctic, high-latitude summer temperatures only are about 1.5° to 2.0°C (2.7–3.6°F) warmer than they were in the mid-20th century, thereby placing us only a quarter of the way to a norm that reigned for three millennia, at least in the Eurasian Arctic.

In recent years, the Arctic Ocean has lost as much as 40 percent of its late-summer ice. The biggest changes take place when the ice is at its seasonal minimum in September. Eventually, it should get sufficiently warm that in some years it will lose much more. This obviously will be disastrous for the polar bear—or so we are repeatedly told. Will it?

Those 3,000 years span several intervals when the Arctic Ocean was nearly—or completely—ice free by the end of summer. In 2008, the Geological Survey of Norway reported upon data gathered from datable beach ridges in northern Greenland. They concluded that there had been little if any late summer ice in the Arctic Ocean 6,000–7,000 years ago.[4]

Martin Jakobsson and his colleagues at Stockholm University write, "Considering these different lines of evidence, a picture begins to emerge suggesting that Arctic sea ice cover was strongly

[3] Glen M. MacDonald et al., "Holocene Treeline History and Climate Change across Northern Eurasia," *Quaternary Research* 53 (2000): 302–11.

[4] Geological Survey of Norway, "Less Ice in Arctic Ocean 6000–7000 Years Ago," October 20, 2008, *Science Daily*, http://www.sciencedaily.com/releases /2008/10/081020095850.htm.

reduced during most of the early Holocene [the post ice-age period]; there appears even to have been periods of ice-free summers in large parts of the central Arctic Ocean."[5]

Another team of Scandinavian researchers, using a computer model coupled to changes in solar radiation conclude, "The increased insolation [solar radiation] during EHIM [Early Holocene (post ice-age) Insolation Maximum] has the potential to push the Arctic Ocean sea ice cover into a regime dominated by seasonal ice, i.e., ice-free summers."[6]

It gets even better. Ice core data from Greenland reveal a very unstable climate from 12,700 to 14,700 years ago. That is *within* the ice age. According to their results, the authors speculate that this instability may be linked to dual stability modes of the Arctic sea ice cover characterized by transitions between periods with and without perennial sea ice cover. In other words, even in the ending phase of the ice age, there were periods of ice-free summers in the Arctic Ocean.

These findings should put to bed the notion that human-induced climate changes in the Arctic will be irreversible. It's also obvious the polar bear has weathered—and maybe even prospered during— many periods when Arctic summer's end was ice free.

Lukewarmers find the fact that the Arctic was ice free for long stretches (both before the end of the last ice age and afterward) to be a compelling argument against the concern for survivability of the iconic polar bear.

---

[5] Martin Jakobsson et al., "New Insights on Arctic Quatenary Climate Variability from Palaeo-Records and Numerical Modelling," *Quaternary Science Reviews* 29 (2010): 3349–58.

[6] Christian Strannea et al., "Arctic Ocean Perennial Sea Ice Breakdown during the Early Holocene Insolation Maximum," *Quaternary Science Reviews* 92 (2014): 123–32.

37. The End of the Apocalypse

> It is now pretty clearly agreed that the CO_2 content [in the atmosphere] will rise 25 percent by 2000. This could increase the average temperature near the earth's surface by 7 degrees Fahrenheit. This in turn could raise the level of the sea by 10 feet. Goodbye, New York. Goodbye, Washington, for that matter.
>
> —Daniel Moynihan*

It is increasingly apparent that warming has been over-forecast, that we can't really do anything about it with today's political and technological realities (see Chapter 39), and that people—especially affluent ones—are pretty darned resilient and adaptive. But there is one fear left. Can global warming induce a rapid melting of the Greenland ice cap? If Greenland's ice cap were to completely disappear, its melting would raise global sea level approximately 23 feet. The principal monger of this particular worry is none other than now-retired NASA scientist James E. Hansen. He's testified, under oath, that much of that rise could take place by the year 2100. He's still at it.[1, 2]

---

*Daniel Patrick Moynihan (1927–2003) was three times reelected to the U.S. Senate (D-NY), joining it in 1976. At the time of this statement in 1969, he was serving President Richard M. Nixon as counselor for urban affairs. He had previously directed the Harvard-MIT Joint Center for Urban Studies. He went on to be ambassador to India (1973–75) and was appointed by President Gerald Ford as U.S. ambassador to the UN (1975–76) prior to his election to the Senate. He was a brilliant, witty, and insightful man, which shows how compelling glib scenarios of disaster must be.

[1] James E. Hansen et al., "Ice Melt, Sea Level Rise, and Superstorms: Evidence from Paleoclimate Data, Climate Modeling, and Modern Observations That 2°C Global Warming Is Highly Dangerous," *Atmospheric Chemistry and Physics: Discussions* 15 (2015): 20059–179.

Hansen made it quite clear in a July 2015 telephone conference call that the purpose of this non-peer-reviewed essay was to influence the upcoming IPCC Paris conference. It's a reprise of his previously discredited and irresponsible disaster mongering, with which we have dealt before (http://www.cato.org/blog/current-wisdom-hansens-extreme-sea-level-rise-projections-drowning-hubris).

[2] Here, Hansen revives the no-longer-fashionable notion of a sudden collapse of the West Antarctic ice sheet. For a thorough and recent debunking of that chestnut, see Rud Istvan's analysis on Judith Curry's blog *Climate Etc.*, http://judithcurry.com/2014/05/18/sea-level-rise-tipping-points.

As discussed in the previous chapter, it was very warm at the onset of the current interglacial and much warmer in the Arctic than it is today. But what happened during the previous interglacial period, that one between the last two major glaciations?

There are multiple lines of evidence that it was even warmer at the beginning of the penultimate interglacial than it was in the current interglacial. Until recently, it had been thought that Greenland was some 2–3°C (3.6–5.4°F) warmer than it is today during a period called the Eemian. The warmth appears to have been concentrated in a 6,000-year period approximately 122,000–128,000 years ago.

Climatologists and others really wanted to know what happened to Greenland's ice cap, but it wasn't until 2013 that researchers finally, literally, got to the bottom of the story. Dorthe Dahl-Jensen and a large team from the Center for Ice and Climate in the Niels Bohr Institute at the University of Copenhagen drilled to the bottom of the ice in northwestern Greenland, providing us with the first climate history of Greenland that includes the warmest period in the last interglacial.[3]

By measuring the ratio of two isotopes of oxygen (specifically ^{18}O and the much more common ^{16}O), one can infer the air temperature at the time the snow crystallized in each annual layer. This is a technique used for decades and considered to be quite reliable. It correlates well with other temperature proxies that Dahl-Jensen used. She found that the average summer temperature calculated from the Eemian maximum ice core peaked at a whopping 8 ± 4°C above the 20th century average. That's 7–22°F warmer than the most recent 1,000 years. And still the ice survived.

The research revealed that the top of the ice was only 130 ± 300 meters lower than today, or a range of from 557 feet higher to 1,411 feet lower than today. By way of perspective, the entire ice core went about 8,000 feet deep.

The loss of ice at the drilling site, which is one of the coldest locations in Greenland, was about 10 percent. But Dahl-Jensen notes that there would be additional losses at lower elevations where the ice is thinner. She says her results are consistent with leaving a bit more than 70 percent of Greenland's remaining total ice intact at the end of the 6,000-year Eemian.

---

[3] D. Dahl-Jensen et al., "Eemian Interglacial Reconstructed from a Greenland Folded Ice Core," *Nature* 493 (2013): 489–94.

Her research findings herald the end of climate apocalypse.

According to a graphic in the paper, the entire 6,000-year period averaged about 6°C warmer in summer than the past 1,000 years. The integrated heating in the region during the Eemian maximum would therefore have been approximately 36,000 "degree-summers" (temperature change multiplied by time). Climate models of our future show a summer warming of about 3°C over northwestern Greenland by around 2100. That's 300 degree-summers per century. With that kind of heating, it would take 12,000 summers to melt a bit less than 30 percent of the ice. It would take about 40,000 summers to melt all of it, which we safely can say is impossible because another ice age will intervene in the meantime.

Evidence suggests that sea levels during the Eemian were about 4–8 meters (13–26 feet) higher than today. Prior to this study, it generally was accepted that the vast majority of that rise came from loss of Greenland's ice. But now, Dahl-Jensen cautiously asserts, somehow more ice than previously thought was lost from Antarctica. Make certain you file that in your "the science is settled" file.

The notion of an alarming rise in the ocean as a result of the loss of Greenland's ice in our immediate future always has been difficult to entertain. Greenland is really cold and any melting should take a very long time—thousands of years—to do very much.

Yet, in a pattern we have repeatedly experienced over the last two decades, no sooner are we about to go to press with our own publication than we read of yet another paper that must be factored into the apocalypse mix. The latest is a complex and touchy simulation by Robert DeConto of the University of Massachusetts and David Pollard at Pennsylvania State University, published online March 30, 2016.[4]

DeConto and Pollard received above-the-fold, front-page coverage in the *New York Times*. Their findings appear to shrink the time for Antarctic melting raising sea levels over 10 feet over the course of a century from roughly the 50th century to the 22nd!

Before readers get all *On The Beach*-y about this, perhaps they should ask themselves if it is possible there are devils hiding in the paper's details. Indeed, there's a veritable forest of impish horns hidden in the dense, but precise prose published in *Nature*.

---

[4] Robert M. DeConto and David Pollard, "Contribution of Antarctica to Past and Future Sea-Level Rise," *Nature* 531 (2016): 591–7.

Each prediction of climate disaster relies on some form of climate model to project future temperature. DeConto and Pollard chose two—one for the ocean and the other for land. The first is a commonly-employed general circulation model (GCM) with its origin in the National Center for Atmospheric Research in Boulder, Colorado. The second is a less-common, smaller-scale Regional Climate Model (RCM) that the researchers apply over an entire continent (Antarctica).

The two models were used as input to models of ice dynamics, including a new one that takes into account rainfall. It's important to note: it doesn't rain over the vast majority of Antarctica—ever.

They sloshed their hybrid ice dynamics model with its absurd rainfall calculations into the continent's huge glaciers. The consequence was gigantic crevasses cracking truly ginormous hunks of ice off the edges of the continent and into the ocean.

It turns out that their "new" ice dynamics model is extremely sensitive. It contains a large number and variety of handles and knobs that are "set"—settings at which one only can guess because the physics upon which the model is based are not well developed. The veracity of a predicted disaster only can be as reliable as the model that is used to predict it. DeConto's and Pope's ice dynamics model is in its infancy and the climate models they've used to generate temperatures for Antarctica are hot—way too hot.

According to Andrew Monaghan of Ohio State University writing in *Geophysical Research Letters*, "20th century (1880–1999) annual Antarctic near-surface air temperature trends in the GCMs are about 2.5-to-5 times larger-than-observed." Monaghan appends this warning, "Until these issues are resolved, IPCC projections for 21st century Antarctic temperature should be regarded with caution." It doesn't appear that the *Times* got that memo. [5]

Buried near the bottom of the supplementary material supplied to *Nature*, one can see how the climate models' overproduction of warming infects DeConto's and Pollard's paper as well. According to the authors, large areas of the entire continent—not just the well-known warming of the tiny Antarctic Peninsula—should have warmed some 7–15°F by now (Figure 51). Only they didn't.

[5] Andrew J. Monaghan, David H. Bromwich, and David P. Schneider, "Twentieth Century Antarctic Air Temperature and Snowfall Simulations by IPCC Climate Models," *Geophysical Research Letters* 35 (2008). doi:10.1029/2007GL032630.

According to Ryan O'Donnell and others writing in the *Journal of Climate* in 2010, summer temperatures have risen since reliable records begin with the 1957 International Geophysical Year, but only about 5–10 percent of what the RCM says should have been happening in many spots (Figure 52).[6]

Figure 51

**Summer Temperature Change
Since Pre-industrial**
(DeConto and Pollard, 2016)

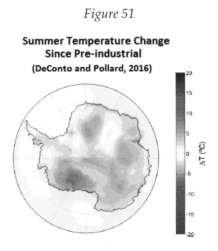

Note: Total temperature change between preindustrial conditions and the present as produced by the climate model DeConto and Pollard used.

A good prediction of climate disaster also requires some guesstimate of how much the concentration of carbon dioxide is going to increase in the future. This paper assumes atmospheric concentrations that even the UN acknowledges to be substantial outliers. DeConto and Pollard let the concentration increase *eight times* above the 19th-century background. We can find only one other paper (back in 1971) using that as a basis for future climate scenarios. We're currently around four-tenths of the way to a doubling.[7]

---

[6] Ryan O'Donnell, et al., "Improved Methods for PCA-Based Reconstructions: Case Study Using the Steig et al. (2009) Antarctic Temperature Reconstruction," *Journal of Climate* 24 (2011): 2099–2115.

[7] S.I. Rasool and Stephen H. Schneider, "Atmospheric Carbon Dioxide and Aerosols: Effects of Large Increases on Global Climate," *Science* 173 (1971): 138–41.

Figure 52

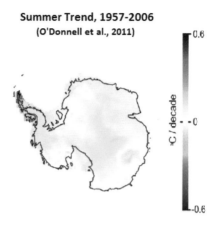

Summer Trend, 1957-2006
(O'Donnell et al., 2011)

Note: Observed trend (°C/decade) in temperature from 1957–2006 determined by O'Donnell and colleagues. Multiply by five (for five decades) to get an idea of the total temperature change since 1957.

There's another scenario in the paper where the increase in carbon dioxide is slower and more realistic, and—shockingly—the end of the world as we know it is delayed by several centuries.

Anyway, after the authors hit "Send"—thereby throwing all of these models into the computer—they compared the results with what (we think) happened during the Eemian. It's there for all to see in Figure 3a in their paper (reproduced in Figure 53): the concatenated models' gargantuan increase in sea level takes place about 1,000 years before it actually was observed. Model fail!

Figure 53

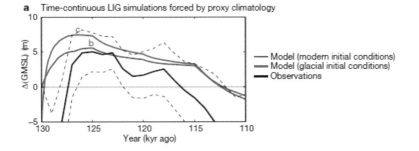

a   Time-continuous LIG simulations forced by proxy climatology

Note: The relevant comparison is between the blue line (modern initial conditions) and the black one (observations of Eemian sea level). The blue line rises dramatically more than a thousand years before the actual sea level rises.

There simply is no reason to believe that this latest Antarctic melting kerfuffle bears any resemblance to reality. By default, that leads us back to Dahl-Jensen. Her ice core extends any potential sea-level crisis at least another 1,000 years into the future. A thousand years probably is far beyond the era in which hydrocarbons will be used for energy production and to produce heat—in other words, forever.

This final tidbit should lay to rest the topic of polar bear survival as explored in Chapter 36. In 2010, Charlotte Lindqvist of the State University of New York–Buffalo sequenced DNA from a polar bear that had been alive before the Eemian. Not only have polar bears survived the warmth at the beginning of the Holocene, but they also survived the Eemian—a time when the integrated warmth in the Arctic was more than 10 times what human activity is able to cause.[8]

---

[8] Charlotte Lindqvist et al., "Complete Mitochondrial Genome of a Pleistocene Jawbone Unveils the Origin of the Polar Bear," *Proceedings of the National Academy of Sciences* 107 (2010): 5053–57.

38. Human Nature

> A mysterious warming of the climate is slowly manifesting itself in the Arctic, engendering a serious international problem.

> —*New York Times* (May 30, 1947)

Fear of the Greenland-driven apocalypse is understandable. So is human inability to accept evidence to the contrary, even when it stares them in the face. Consider the peculiar case of "Warming Island."

In its science section on January 16, 2007, the *New York Times* featured an article by John Collins Rudolph concerning a newly discovered island off the coast of Greenland "long thought to be a part of Greenland's mainland." It turned out to be an island from which a glacier had retreated (Figure 54).

Dennis Schmitt (an explorer from Berkeley, California) "discovered" it in 2005. According to the *Times*, "Schmitt, who speaks Inuit, has provisionally named it 'Uunartoq Qeqertoq: the Warming Island.'"

Figure 54

Note: Landsat data showing the retreat of the ice that eventually uncovered Uunartoq Qeqertoq (Warming Island). Data from 1985 appear on the left, 2002 data are in the middle, and 2005 data are on the right. Note the landform's rather distinctive shape.[1]

---

[1] Landsat Missions, U.S. Geological Survey, http://landsat.usgs.gov/images/gallery/90_L.jpg.

Rudolph went on to speculate:

> Despite its remote location, the island would almost certainly
> have been discovered, named and mapped almost a century
> ago when explorers like Jean-Baptiste Charcot and Philippe,
> Duke of Orléans, charted these coastlines. Would have been
> discovered had it not been bound to the coast by glacial ice.

The *Times* article includes a map showing the location of Uunartoq
Qeqertoq off Carlsbad Fjord in east-central Greenland.

In 2010, we published a paper summarizing southern Greenland's
temperature history dating back to the late-18th century, thanks to a
network of weather stations put in place by the Danish government.
At the time of our writing, the record ended in 2006, around the time
of Schmitt's discovery (Figure 55).

Is Uunartoq Qeqertoq (Warming Island) something new, or was it
simply uncovered during the mid-20th century at a time of greater
integrated warming than had been observed in the years prior to
Schmitt's discovery?

Figure 55

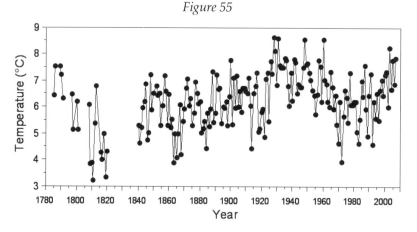

Note: Average temperature of the southern Greenland coastal region, based
upon Danish data. The book *Arctic Riviera* was published in 1957, near the
end of the longest period of persistent warmth in Greenland's thermometric
history.[2]

---

[2] Oliver Frauenfeld et al., "A Reconstruction of Annual Greenland Ice Melt Extent,
1784–2009," *Journal of Geophysical Research: Atmospheres* 116 (2011): D08104.

An Internet search turned up a 1957 book about eastern Greenland by aerial photographer Ernst Hofer with the intriguing title *Arctic Riviera*. Hofer was photographing Greenland in support of various expeditions onto its massive icecap, a job soon to be rendered obsolete by orbiting satellites. The book was published near the end of what appears to have been the warmest period in the 20th century— one in which summer temperatures did not deviate significantly, on average, from what is observed today.[3]

Arctic Riviera contains a map obviously predating its 1957 publication. It shows Carlsbad Fjord and Warming Island. You can identify Uunartoq Qeqertoq in the land and satellite images from its unusual shape (see Figure 56).

Carbon dioxide–related warming likely was very small in the 1950s, so it appears Warming Island is a result of natural causes. The take-home lesson is that Greenland's climate is volatile.

Figure 56

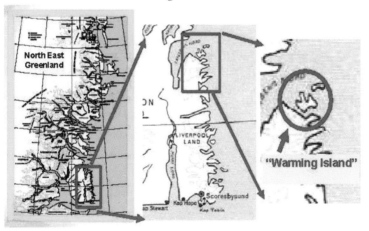

Note: This map from *Arctic Riviera* shows Uunartoq Qeqertoq (Warming Island) to have been an island before 1957.[4]

---

[3] Ernst Hofer, *Arctic Riviera: A Book about the Beauty of Greenland* (Schönbühl Urtenen, Switzerland: Kümmerly & Frey, 1957).

[4] Image adapted from ibid.

Rudolph still maintains Hofer's map is wrong, complaining that it was "hand-drawn." Prior to the digital age, so were all the other original maps on this Earth.[5]

The prolonged mid-20th-century warmth in Greenland has been well noted. Hans Ahlmann, a University of Stockholm geographer, wrote a number of papers describing the changes occurring in the Arctic as a result of the warming in the first half of the 20th century. He often referred to it as a "climate improvement." In a booklet he prepared to accompany his 1952 lecture to the American Geographical Society on glacial variations and climate fluctuations, he describes the rapidly receding glaciers and rising temperatures—as well as large-scale biotic and social changes—across many disparate regions of the Arctic. Ahlmann quotes Denmark's prime minister as proclaiming:

> In the last generation changes that have had a decisive influence on all social life have occurred in Greenland. A new era has begun. These changes are primarily due to two circumstances. Firstly, the Greenland climate has changed, and with it Greenland's natural and economic prospects.[6]

Uunartoq Qeqertoq was an island in the mid-20th century before Schmitt provisionally renamed it. The ice bridge that connected it to the mainland probably was rebuilt during subsequent cooling.

Lukewarmers are aware of the many factors that make it so very hard to abandon belief in disastrous climate change.

---

[5] See Andrew Revkin's *Dot Earth* blog at http://dotearth.blogs.nytimes.com/2008/04/28/arctic-explorer-rebuts-critique-of-warming-island/.

[6] H. W. Ahlmann, *Glacier Variations and Climatic Fluctuations*, Bowman Memorial Lectures, Series 3 (New York: American Geographical Society, 1953). Available from http://www.questia.com/PM.qst?a=o&d=1918470.

39. Climate MAGICC

New York will probably be like Florida 15 years from now.

—*St. Louis Post-Dispatch* (1989)

One thing lukewarmers tend to do is crunch a lot of numbers. We want to know if mitigating global warming by reducing emissions of greenhouse gases is worth the cost. We'd like to know how the price of adaptation will vary under different scenarios of warming.

To facilitate this sort of inquiry, we've adapted for your use the very same model the U.S. Environmental Protection Agency (EPA) employs in calculating the effect of various policy proposals on climate. They call it "Model for the Assessment of Greenhouse Gas–Induced Climate Change." If you play the acronym game you'll note that that renders it MAGICC. Its creator, Tom Wigley, from the University Corporation for Atmospheric Research, came up with the name and acronym; we didn't. You'll find our MAGICC emulator at http://www.cato.org/blog/current-wisdom-we-calculate-you-decide-handy-dandy-carbon-tax-temperature-savings-calculator. Use it to your lukewarm heart's content. All you have to do is choose among three fields of information:

1. The CO_2 emissions reduction amount—calculated from the 2005 baseline—that will take place by the year 2050 and remain in place thereafter.
2. The region of the globe that will take part in the emissions reduction plan—the United States, for example, or for the more optimistic, all industrialized nations of the world.
3. The climate sensitivity, or how much you believe global average temperature will increase as a result of doubling the preindustrial atmospheric CO_2 concentration. EPA's guess is 3.0°C. But, as noted earlier, a growing collection of reports from the recent scientific literature puts the value between 1.5°C and 2.0°C. Not wanting to leave hotheads out of the fun, we include an option of selecting an extremely high climate sensitivity value of 4.5°C.

Once you make your selections, the calculator returns the amount of global temperature rise averted by 2050 and 2100 as a consequence of your choices.

Try this example:

A Handy-Dandy Carbon Tax Temperature-Savings Calculator

Region

◉ U.S.   ○ Industrialized Countries

CO2 Reduction (%)

○ 0   ○ 20   ○ 40   ○ 60   ○ 80   ◉ 100

Climate Sensitivity (C)

○ 1.5   ○ 2   ◉ 3   ○ 4.5

[Submit]

GLOBAL TEMPERATURE RISE AVERTED

2050: 0.052°C

2100: 0.137°C

Note: Cato Institute Center for the Study of Science "MAGICC emulator."[1]

Choose a 100 percent reduction in carbon dioxide emissions by the United States along with EPA's sensitivity value of 3.0°C. Hit "Submit." The amount of temperature savings that results is 0.052°C by 2050 and 0.137°C by 2100. We'll explain why we extend the temperatures to three significant digits in the Appendix to this volume.

Now that you have your answer, you should know that you have chosen the Intergovernmental Panel on Climate Change's 2007 "most

---

[1] See "Current Wisdom: We Calculate, You Decide: A Handy-Dandy Carbon Tax Temperature-Savings Calculator," *Cato at Liberty* (blog), http://www.cato.org/blog /current-wisdom-we-calculate-you-decide-handy-dandy-carbon-tax-temperature -savings-calculator.

likely" value for climate sensitivity, disregarding recent scientific literature. That 2013 report declines to choose a "most likely" value, which is probably a good idea given how things are turning out. As you see, a dramatic cessation of economic activities that create CO_2 emissions reduces the amount of global warming a little more than 0.10°C out of a projected rise of 2.619°C between 2010 and 2100.

Some people (and some libertarians) who haven't thought things through are going around Washington, D.C., advocating for a tax on CO_2 as the best way to reduce emissions. But, as MAGICC shows, why bother? How high would the tax have to be to discourage all emissions? Once they're able to establish that, how will they sell the idea that a rise in global temperature of 2.482°C is vastly preferable to a rise of 2.619°C?

To explore other alternatives, use our handy-dandy MAGICC emulator. If you are a fan of futility, you should have fun.

MAGICC also brings to light the futility of U.S. climate policy given that China's emissions are going to be approximately 2.5 times ours by the time China's energy demand stabilizes and given that India has just announced that it is going to open the largest coal mine on Earth.

40. Damn the MAGICC, Full Speed Ahead

It is error alone which needs the support of government. Truth can stand by itself.

—Thomas Jefferson

Lukewarmers continue to be dismayed by the absolute disregard for logic that pervades the global warming issue. For example, the Obama White House is fully aware that MAGICC says that anything we do—including reducing our CO_2 emissions to zero—will have little-to-no detectable effect on global temperature, even into the next century. That hasn't stopped it from telling federal agencies to institute climate policies and to avoid letting taxpayers in on the futility of it all.

In February 2015, the White House Council on Environmental Quality (CEQ) released a draft guidance that "describes how federal departments and agencies should consider the effects of greenhouse gas emissions and climate change" under reviews mandated by the National Environmental Policy Act—a 1970 law that requires an assessment of the environmental impacts of any proposed major federal action.

The CEQ guidelines make clear that it doesn't want the climate change impacts to be described using measures of climate—things like temperature, precipitation, storm intensity, storm frequency, and the like. Rather, agencies simply are to state the quantity of emissions this or that action will forgo.

CEQ seeks to confine the climate change discussion to greenhouse gases in order to disguise the fact that each and every federal agency action—either individually or across the entire government—is a complete and utter waste of time in terms of climate change impact. That's the last thing the White House wants to say and it prefers not to admit at all.

The executive budgeteers at the Office of Management and Budget (OMB) require agencies to calculate costs and benefits of proposed environmental regulation. They root the cost side of their equation in a method cooked up (we choose our words carefully) in a highly technical document produced by the Interagency Working Group (IWG). The working group concocted something they call the "social cost of carbon." It's a calculation of how much each ton of CO_2 emissions theoretically will cost in terms of negative effects. That's where things begin to get dodgy.

OMB issued a series of guidelines regarding how to calculate the social cost of carbon. Consider this one. It's pretty much in colloquial English (or as close to it as a noneditorial GS-11 is able to express him- or herself):

> Your analysis should focus on benefits and costs that accrue to citizens and residents of the United States. Where you choose to evaluate a regulation that is likely to have effects beyond the borders of the United States, these effects should be reported separately.[1]

This explicit directive didn't faze the IWG. It reports a *global* value of the social cost of carbon that, it says, accrues from continued CO_2 emissions in the United States. It chooses to ignore OMB's instruction to instead "focus on benefits and costs that accrue to citizens and residents of the United States." The IWG bases its social cost of carbon on its own determination of "effects beyond the borders of the United States."

Even for federal work, this is bizarre. Federal agencies are proposing regulations *within* the United States, but are reporting only *global* costs and making no determination of the *domestic* ones.

This is inappropriate, but it is required in order to generate a high social cost, because the IWG is fully aware that climate change is a minor overlay atop an affluent and vibrant society like ours.

The IWG also is in direct violation of another explicit OMB directive regarding the important discount rate. OMB states that a "real discount rate of 7 percent" should be used as a base case for regulatory analysis. To show the sensitivity of the results to the discount

---

[1] OMB Circular A-4 (September 17, 2003) regarding regulatory analysis.

rate assumptions for regulatory analysis, "you should provide estimates of net benefits using both 3 percent and 7 percent."[2, 3]

Instead, the working group opted to determine the social cost of carbon using discount rates of 2.5, 3.0, and 5.0 percent. It chose not to include results for a 7.0 percent discount rate calculation. We suspect this is because a 7.0 percent rate for regulating CO_2 confers a negative cost (or a benefit) if one assumes the recent lukewarm estimates of climate sensitivity.

The administration is in denial concerning new scientific literature indicating a decreased sensitivity. It refuses to acknowledge that a major paper written by 15 authors of the 2013 Intergovernmental Panel on Climate Change report greatly reduces the sensitivity and cuts off warming's fat tail. This administration simply is denying the growing (and embarrassing) disparity between what climate models say should already have happened in the lower atmosphere and what actually is happening. It simply refuses to consider a massive increase in global food production worth $3.2 trillion as a direct and beneficial result of increasing the atmospheric concentration of CO_2.[4]

This has ramifications for any number of federal regulatory agencies. When the Department of Energy proposed an efficiency guideline for microwave ovens on June 13, 2013, it calculated the benefits of the regulation by citing the Intergovernmental Working Group's dodgy calculation of the social cost of carbon. It didn't display the costs with OMB's mandated 7 percent discount rate because the IWG didn't use it!

---

[2] The April 16, 2015, edition of *The Economist* blog *Free Exchange* contains a pretty nifty explanation of what a discount rate is (and why it is important) in an article titled, "Very Long Run Discount Rates: Not So Impatient."

> Most people would prefer to receive a gift now, instead of the same one in 20 years' time. Economists refer to this notion by speaking of "discount rates," the rate at which future costs and benefits are adjusted in order to make them comparable with those today. If, for example, you are indifferent between receiving $100 today or $105 in one year's time, you "discount" future consumption at a rate of 5 percent.

[3] OMB's Circular A-4 refers to Circular A-94, the document in which the OMB directive is made.

[4] A five-minute video on the Cato Institute's Center for the Study of Science's July 22, 2015, presentation to the U.S. Congress concerning problems with the science problems is available at http://www.cato.org/multimedia/media-highlights-tv /patrick-j-michaels-testifies-committee-natural-resources-hearing.

The Obama administration will continue to accelerate regulation of CO_2 despite the absence of legislative assent and while using jimmied models to calculate the social cost of carbon. It's on a mission . . . from Paris.

41. Paris, December 12, 2015

> It's just b***t for them to say: "We'll have a 2°C warming target and then try to do a little better every five years." It's just worthless words. There is no action, just promises.
>
> —James Hansen, December 12, 2016

At 1:30 p.m. on Saturday, December 12, the French presidency—charged with running the Paris summit—presented to those in attendance the final text of a proposed agreement. Adoption was to come upon a rubber stamp vote.

The final text expressed the goal of a total warming of "well below 2°C above preindustrial levels and pursuing efforts to limit the temperature increase to 1.5 °C." How it is the negotiators failed to recognize the simple reality that the United Nation's (UN) own climate models reveal the second aspirational target—that of limiting the temperature increase to 1.5 °C—is impossible to achieve? That's because it doesn't permit any further emission of carbon dioxide, whatsoever.

The U.S. chief negotiator, Secretary of State John Kerry, found a major problem in Article 4.4, which read:

> Developed country Parties *shall* continue taking the lead by undertaking economy-wide absolute emission reduction targets. Developing country Parties should continue enhancing their mitigation efforts, and are encouraged to move over time towards economy-wide emission reduction or limitation targets in the light of different national circumstances. [emphasis added]

In other words, under the agreement as written, the United States would be agreeing to be bound by a treaty. Such language ("shall") caused the agreement to cross a line that—like its failed predecessor, the Kyoto Protocol—would guarantee it never, ever could gain approval by the two-thirds of the U.S. Senate required under Article II of the U.S. Constitution to ratify a treaty.

To change the wording, the United States would be forced to object from the floor of the convention. That likely would open up nitpicking by dozens of other nations and possibly delay the close of the meeting by several days. It might even scuttle the entire agreement.

The developing nations were adamant that the word "shall" applied to the United States and that the language applicable to developed nations should remain "should." Further, "shall" should not apply to everyone.

The United States insisted that "shall" was a mistake and informed the European Union (EU) participants that the U.S. Constitution requires a two-thirds majority of the Senate to adopt such a "shall document." Were it to become a "should document" it would function as an executive agreement.

Six hours later, the French decided that use of the word "shall" was the result of a typo. Kerry was able to escape Paris without binding the United States to a treaty. Instead, he left with a lukewarm agreement.

The final document consists of a long (19-page) preamble citing the reasons for the resulting Paris Agreement to which the signatories agree. The agreement contains the following important provisions:

- The objective is stated to be: "Holding the increase in the global average temperature to well below 2°C above preindustrial levels and to pursue efforts to limit the temperature increase to 1.5°C above preindustrial levels." (Article 2, Section 1a)
- Each country's proposed "contribution" to emissions reductions is to be resubmitted every five years. Each revised contribution is to "represent a progression beyond" the previous. (Article 4, Sections 3 and 9)
- Nations will report their emissions under no new standard. In other words, the same lax procedures that have applied to the developing world will continue to apply. (Article 4, Sections 13 and 14)
- "Developed country Parties shall provide financial resources to assist developing country Parties with respect to both mitigation and adaptation in continuation of their existing obligations under the Convention." While this would appear to make the agreement a binding treaty (by virtue of the use of the word "shall"), in reality what it says is that the financial assistance the

developed world already agreed to provide in the original (1992) Framework Convention on Climate Change will continue. This merely affirms an existing treaty. (Article 9, Section 1)

- The mechanism used to "promote compliance" is to be "transparent, non-adversarial, and non-punitive." In other words, nations that fail to fulfill their "determined contributions" are not going to be punished in any manner. This renders the agreement unenforceable. (Article 15, Sections 1 and 2)

- Signatories may withdraw from the Agreement at any time after it has been in force for three years. (Article 28)

The Paris Agreement is an unenforceable document that requires its signatories to prepare new "determined contributions" every five years, counts *all* warming since the Industrial Revolution as having been caused by greenhouse gas emissions, and—because it uses the mean sensitivity of the UN climate models—requires an immediate cessation of all carbon dioxide emissions to meet its aspirational goal of 1.5°C of total warming.

Oren Cass of the Manhattan Institute testified to Congress in December 2015 about the true nature of the "determined contributions" in the Paris Agreement. The notion that they will have a significant effect on warming turns out to be fatuous.

The popular tracking programs used by the UN to determine the effects of the Intended Nationally Determined Contributions (INDCs) assume they impose reductions from the UN's highest emission scenario, the RCP 8.5. RCP is an acronym for Representative Concentration Pathway, a method of expressing a net change in warming radiation in the lower atmosphere by 2100. "RCP 8.5" is the largest possible change and represents an increase of 8.5 watts. According to the UN, "The RCP 8.5 has higher emissions than all but a few published baseline scenarios."

Observed emissions trends, coupled with the anticipated worldwide exploitation of shale gas, certainly argue for a lower number— likely something around three-fourths of RCP 8.5. That would result in an emissions trajectory very much like what the UN calls in its 2001 Intergovernmental Panel on Climate Change (IPCC) scientific assessment a "midrange" emissions scenario.

Cass referred in his testimony to calculations made by Climate Interactive, a Washington nonprofit working with the U.S. Department of State, Climate Action Tracker (an online calculator), and the Massachusetts Institute of Technology. Even accepting the unrealistically high emissions scenario, Cass noted:

> In aggregate, the best estimate for [the total] temperature rise [to 2100] with INDCs appears to be 3.5°C (Climate Interactive) to 3.7°C (MIT), while the best estimate of the world's trajectory absent them is 3.6°C (Climate Action Tracker current policy) to 3.9°C (MIT). In other words, the actual improvement if all countries follow through with their voluntary contributions, is 0.1 to 0.2°C.

> However, even this estimate may overstate the impact of the INDCs.[1]

The amount of 21st century warming in the IPCC's midrange scenario depends upon the sensitivity of temperature to an effective doubling of carbon dioxide. In Figure 57, we show three examples. The first (green) is for 3.0°C, a temperature that is very close to the mean sensitivity of the IPCC model suite of 3.2°C. However, the recent spate of low-sensitivity estimates averages 2.0°C (yellow). A closer value as calculated by Nic Lewis is 1.6°C (red), as we discussed in Chapter 18.

The "midrange" scenario is one of rapid economic development in which efficient technologies are discovered and adopted. Shale gas is a perfect example of this and demonstrates the likelihood that we already are on this trajectory.

Note, too, that the total predicted warming—even using the highest-sensitivity assumption—is less than that calculated from the INDCs by the various trackers. The only logical conclusion is that what was agreed to in Paris is what was going to happen anyway.

Some very big emitters are playing very fast-and-loose with their INDCs. In Beijing in 2014, President Obama made a big deal out of China's intention to hold its emissions constant "around 2030" in their INDC even though the U.S. Department of Energy already had published a paper in 2011 that showed, absent any major emissions reduction program, that is what was likely to happen in China anyway.

---

[1] Oren M. Cass, senior fellow, Manhattan Institute for Policy Research, Testimony before the House Committee on Science, Space, and Technology, 114th Cong., 1st sess., December 1, 2015, http://docs.house.gov/meetings/SY/SY00/20151201/104257/HHRG-114-SY00-Wstate-CassO-20151201.pdf.

Figure 57

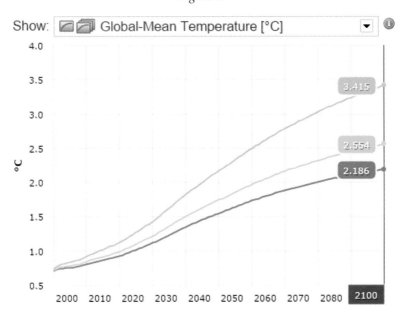

Note: Projected global average surface temperature trajectories for the 2001 IPCC midrange emissions scenario. Three sensitivities are shown: 3.0°C, 2.0°C, and 1.6°C. Note that these calculations are likely themselves to be in error because they attribute almost all of the warming since 1900 to carbon dioxide. The warming of the early 20th century is likely to have had another cause.

China's INDC goes on to say it will reduce its emissions by 60–65 percent per unit of GDP between 2005 and 2030. China has only recently revealed that it already has underestimated its 21st century coal use by up to 17 percent. By revising its early 21st century emissions upward, it renders its proposed reduction in emissions per unit of GDP to probably less than would occur absent any policy whatsoever. According to Cass:

> Climate Action Tracker, one of the organizations attempting to calculate INDC impacts, provides a China-specific view and projects the country's commitments to fall squarely in the middle of the projection for current policy (i.e., absent the INDC).

India's INDC is even more of a joke. India proposes to reduce emissions per unit of GDP by 33–35 percent between 2005–2030, a change that would average 1.4 percent per year. However, from 2005–2012, India's emissions/GDP already had declined by 17 percent, or 2.1 percent per year (Figure 58). Indeed, India has voluntarily pledged to reduce its emissions per unit GDP at a *slower* rate than if it simply continued along its business-as-usual path.

Figure 58

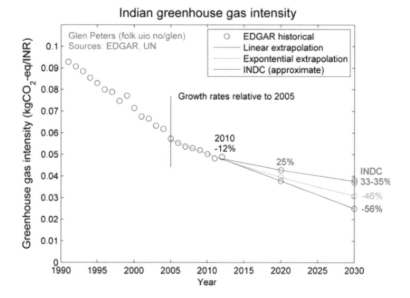

Note: India's INDC (red) clearly accomplishes less than if it simply continued its business as-usual pathway (blue).

China and India provide perfect examples of why warming under the Paris Agreement will be even greater than the IPCC's midrange emissions scenario, a rate of emissions that generally is considered to be what is likely to happen absent this ineffectual climate agreement.

When all is said and done, if one uses the most likely values for sensitivity, the Paris Agreement results in a reduction in potential warming that is operationally meaningless and results in a lukewarm agreement fit for a lukewarm world. Only the United States and the EU stand to be harmed.

42. Paris's Last Tango?

> "If the U.S. Supreme Court actually declares the coal power plant rules stillborn, the chances of nurturing trust between countries would all but vanish," said Navroz K. Dubash, a senior fellow at the Center for Policy Research in New Delhi. "This could be the proverbial string which causes Paris to unravel."
>
> *New York Times,* December 10, 2016

At the Paris conference, China told the world it would try to peak its carbon dioxide emissions at precisely the time U.S. economists predicted they would peak years before the conference began. India said it would emit more than "business-as-usual." In fact, among the large economies, only the European Union and the United States stated an "intention" to go considerably beyond their prior commitments. The United States intends a 26–28 percent emissions cut below 2005 levels by 2025 while the EU targets a 24 percent cut in the same timeframe.

The largest portion of U.S. reduction is to come from President Obama's "Clean Power Plan." A draft of the proposed plan—published in June 2014—made it seem it would be rather benign. It appeared to achieve a 32 percent reduction in electricity-related emissions largely by replacing coal generation with natural gas. Gas-fueled plants are easier to build and less costly to operate than are coal-fired plants. It's also expected the price of natural gas will remain competitive due to an abundance of gas that can be tapped by hydraulic fracturing of shale deposits.

However, the final version of the Clean Power Plan (CPP), when it was unveiled in August 2015, differed dramatically from the earlier draft.

The United States currently produces about 31 percent of its electricity using natural gas. The CPP only lets that rise to 33 percent. The balance of demand for electricity is to come from installation of unreliable, pricey, subsidized, and heavily propagandized solar and windmill generation technologies.

The Obama Administration bases its sweeping reformation of our national energy supply structure on an obscure section of the Clean Air Act Amendments of 1990—a provision that is itself in conflict with another equally obscure section of the Act. In a 2014 case that was taken up by the U.S. Supreme Court and concerned regulation of power plant emissions, Justice Antonin Scalia served notice he didn't think this was a good idea:

> When an agency claims to discover in a long-extant statute an unheralded power to regulate "a significant portion of the American economy," we [the Court] typically greet its announcement with a measure of skepticism. We expect Congress to speak clearly if it wishes to assign to an agency decisions of vast "economic and political significance."

On February 9, 2016, the Supreme Court—on a 5-4 vote—placed a "stay" on implementation of the CPP. Up to that time, a U.S. District Court had been letting the CPP stand while an appeal concerning the Clean Air Act's two conflicting clauses progressed. There was a strong probability that whatever the district court finally decided likely would result in a petition for a Writ of Certiorari to the Supreme Court. In that context, it seemed the court's 5-4 vote would mean the four votes necessary to grant Certiorari were likely.

Going a step further, the 5-4 vote on the stay could well have signaled that the Supreme Court was likely—given the majority's warning in the 2014 power plant case—to side with the petitioners and throw out the CPP. But we'll never know. Four days after the vote, Justice Scalia died in his room at the Cibolo Creek Ranch during a hunting trip to the Chinati Mountains of west Texas.

The CPP is central to the success of the U.S. reduction plan as submitted in Paris. As a consequence, whether or not the CPP survives likely will be determined by voters on November 8, 2016, when they elect the president who will nominate Justice Scalia's replacement on the court.

It would appear the fate of the Paris Agreement lies in the hands of the American electorate.

Appendix: Notes on the MAGICC Model

The results from our MAGICC emulator are produced from climate change calculations performed using the Model for the Assessment of Greenhouse Gas–Induced Climate Change (MAGICC) climate model simulator. MAGICC was developed by scientists at the National Center for Atmospheric Research with funding from the Environmental Protection Agency.

MAGICC is a collection of simple gas-cycle, climate, and ice-melt models used to efficiently emulate the output of complex climate models. MAGICC produces projections of global average temperature and sea-level change under user-configurable emissions scenarios and model parameters. MAGICC is run using default model parameter settings, except for climate sensitivity from which the user can choose between 1.5°C and 4.5°C.

The baseline emissions scenario against which all carbon dioxide reductions are measured is scenario A1B from the Intergovernmental Panel on Climate Change's (IPCC) Special Report on Emissions Scenarios (SRES).

Scenario A1B is a middle-of-the-road emissions pathway that assumes rapid CO_2 emissions growth during the first half of the 21st century and a slow CO_2 emissions decline thereafter. Emissions are prescribed by country groups. The Cato Institute's "Industrialized Countries" group comprises the OECD90 countries: North America, western Europe, Australia, New Zealand, and Japan.

In order to obtain the U.S. baseline emissions to which the emissions reduction schedule can be applied, U.S. emissions were backed out of the OECD90 country grouping. The current percentage of total group emissions contributed by the United States was determined. That turned out to be right around 50 percent. We assume this percentage will remain constant over time. In other words, the United States contributed 50 percent of the OECD90 emissions in 2000 and will continue to do so in every year between 2000 and 2100.

In this way, the U.S. future emissions pathway was developed from the group pathway defined by the IPCC under the A1B scenario.

From these baselines (either U.S. or OECD90), CO_2 emissions reductions were linearly applied from 2005–2050 to obtain a user-specified total reduction. The new (reduced) emissions were recombined with the other (unadjusted) IPCC country groupings to produce the global emissions total. It is total global emissions that are entered into MAGICC to yield global temperature projections. The results using the reduced emissions pathway are then compared to the results using the original A1B pathway as prescribed by the IPCC, with the baseline against which temperature changes are calculated set to 2010.

We assume that other actions that occur as a result of reducing CO_2 emissions are a wash. We recognize that reducing combustion of fossil fuels will result in co-impacts such as reduced emissions of carbon monoxide, volatile organic compounds, nitrogen oxides, and sulfur oxides. The first three generally enhance warming; the latter generally retards it. Sensitivity tests using MAGICC indicate that for the OECD90 countries under the A1B pathway, the effects largely cancel out one another.

And here's that additional fine print on precision we promised: we presented our temperature savings in three significant digits in order to tell them apart from each other. In the real world, the impacts from the emissions reduction pathways are not nearly so precise. In fact, the temperature savings from most of the different CO_2 emissions reduction pathways are scientifically impossible to differentiate and, in many cases, impossible to differentiate from the original A1B scenario. In sum, they all are—for some time to come—the same as doing nothing. They are so nugatory as to require three significant digits.

Index

A page number followed by *f* indicate figures; *t* indicates tables; *n* indicates footnotes.

About the Author

Patrick J. Michaels is director of the Cato Institute's Center for the Study of Science and spent 30 years as a research professor of environmental sciences at the University of Virginia. He is a past president of the American Association of State Climatologists and former program chair for the Committee on Applied Climatology of the American Meteorological Society.

Paul C. "Chip" Knappenberger is assistant director for Cato's Center for the Study of Science. He has over 25 years of experience in climate research and public outreach, including 10 years with the Virginia State Climatology Office and 15 years as the research coordinator for New Hope Environmental Services.

Cato Institute

Founded in 1977, the Cato Institute is a public policy research foundation dedicated to broadening the parameters of policy debate to allow consideration of more options that are consistent with the principles of limited government, individual liberty, and peace. To that end, the Institute strives to achieve greater involvement of the intelligent, concerned lay public in questions of policy and the proper role of government.

The Institute is named for Cato's Letters, libertarian pamphlets that were widely read in the American Colonies in the early 18th century and played a major role in laying the philosophical foundation for the American Revolution.

Despite the achievement of the nation's Founders, today virtually no aspect of life is free from government encroachment. A pervasive intolerance for individual rights is shown by government's arbitrary intrusions into private economic transactions and its disregard for civil liberties. And while freedom around the globe has notably increased in the past several decades, many countries have moved in the opposite direction, and most governments still do not respect or safeguard the wide range of civil and economic liberties.

To address those issues, the Cato Institute undertakes an extensive publications program on the complete spectrum of policy issues. Books, monographs, and shorter studies are commissioned to examine the federal budget, Social Security, regulation, military spending, international trade, and myriad other issues. Major policy conferences are held throughout the year, from which papers are published thrice yearly in the Cato Journal. The Institute also publishes the quarterly magazine Regulation.

In order to maintain its independence, the Cato Institute accepts no government funding. Contributions are received from foundations, corporations, and individuals, and other revenue is generated from the sale of publications. The Institute is a nonprofit, tax-exempt, educational foundation under Section 501(c)3 of the Internal Revenue Code.

CATO INSTITUTE
1000 Massachusetts Ave., N.W.
Washington, D.C. 20001
www.cato.org